Technology of Skilled Processes

Basic Engineering Competences

Fabrication

Editorial Panel

C Oakey, HNC, FTC
Section Leader – Fabrication and Motor Vehicle Engineering
Dewsbury and Batley Technical and Art College

V Green, TEng(CEI), MBIM
Head of Department of Engineering Crafts
Huddersfield Technical College

C Sutcliffe, OBE, MSc, CEng, MIMechE
Vocational Curriculum Services
City and Guilds of London Institute

Published as a
co-operative venture
between
Stam Press Ltd

and

City and Guilds

Syllabus

Technology of Skilled Processes 367-1

Section	Process	Section	Process
1	Observing Safe Practices	8	Joining
2	Moving Loads	9	Fabrication
3	Measurement and Dimensional Control (1)	10	Soft Soldering, Hard Soldering and Brazing
4	Marking Out	11	Fusion Welding
5	Work and Toolholding	12	Power Transmission
6	Removing Material	13	Assembly and Dismantling (1)
7	Forming	14	Interpreting Drawings, Specifications and Data

Syllabus

Basic Engineering Competences 201

Basic Engineering Technology
201-1-01
01 Industrial Studies
02 Observing Safe Practices
03 Moving Loads
04 Measurement and Dimensional Control (1)
05 Marking Out
06 Work and Toolholding
07 Removing Material
08 Joining
09 Interpreting Drawings, Specifications and Data
010 Assembly and Dismantling (1)

Basic Fabrication and Welding Technology
201-1-07
01 Forming
02 Fabrication
03 Soft Soldering, Hard Soldering and Brazing
04 Fusion Welding

Basic Maintenance Technology
201-1-09
01 Forming
02 Soft Soldering, Hard Soldering and Brazing
03 Power Transmission
04 Measurement and Testing of Electro-Mechanical Systems (1)

Science Background to Technology
201-1-04
01 Basic Physical Quantities, Electricity and Magnetism
02 Forces
03 Pressure
04 The Principles of Tool Construction; Materials Technology

SUPPORTING BOOKS

Book titles	Covering	Covering
Basic Engineering	**Syllabus** 367-1	Syllabus 201-1-01
Observing Safe Practices and Moving Loads	Sections 1 and 2	02-03
Measuring and Marking Out	Sections 3 and 4	04-05
Workholding and Toolholding: Removing Material	Sections 5 and 6	06-07
Joining	Section 8	08
Interpreting Drawings, Specifications and Data	Section 14	09
Assembling and Dismantling	Section 13	10
Fabrication and Welding		Syllabus 201-1-07
Forming	Section 7	01
Fabrication	Section 9	02
Soft Soldering, Hard Soldering and Brazing	Section 10	03
Fusion Welding	Section 11	04
Maintenance		Syllabus 201-1-09
Forming	Section 7	01
Soft Soldering, Hard Soldering and Brazing	Section 10	02
Power Transmission	Section 12	03
Science		Syllabus 201-1-04
Basic Physical Quantities, Electricity and Magnetism		01
Forces		02
Pressure		03
The principles of Tool Construction; Materials Technology		04

Syllabus

201 – Basic Engineering Competences
201-1-07 Basic Fabrication and Welding Technology

02 Basic Competence in Fabrication

The contents of this book have been designed to cover the requirements of the City and Guilds Basic Fabrication and Welding Technology 201-1-07 (02).

As listed, the heading references in this book conform with those in the 201 scheme. The contents equally well cover Section 9 of the Technology of Skilled Processes scheme 367-1.

Contents Fabrication

4 Introduction

This book is intended for those who are, or will be, doing a practical job in industry.

It is specially written for those who need their technology as a background to their work and as a means of adapting to changes in working practices caused by technological advance. Where words such as 'he' or 'crafstman' appear in this series, they are to be interpreted as 'he/she', 'crafstman/craftswoman'.

This new series of textbooks presents the technology in terms of competence rather than working from a conventional theoretical base, i.e. the material will help readers understand:

- the use of
- the change to
- the development of
- other uses of

industrial process technology and skills.

This book has been compiled after a survey of the industrial skilled processes which form the nucleus of occupational schemes and pre-vocational courses of the City and Guilds of London Institute and a comparison with provisions elsewhere in Europe.

Three basic facts emerged:

- the technology is common to many different schemes though the contexts of applications are very different;
- the technology is being taught in a variety of workshops in a variety of exercises related to the immediate needs of students and their industries; these industrially-related exercises formed excellent learning tasks and provided clear motivation for students because of their immediate relevance;
- the technology is so well integrated with the 'first-task need' that students did not recognise its relevance to many other tasks they would be called upon to perform.

This book seeks to build on the learning tasks and to provide a means of learning and generalising the technology, so that the immediate job is better understood and better done, new tasks using the same process technology are more quickly mastered and updating or retraining is easier and more effective.

The editors are grateful to the British Standards Institution for allowing the use of extracts from their publications. They welcome constructive suggestions which should be addressed to:

Stanley Thornes (Publishers) Ltd.
Old Station Drive, Leckhampton, Cheltenham, Gloucestershire
GL53 0DN

ACKNOWLEDGEMENTS

The publishers gladly record their thanks to the following contributors who have kindly supplied material for inclusion in this book:

Longman Group Ltd.,: *Fabrication and Welding* by W. Kenyon; The Engineering Industry Training Board; J. and E. Hall Ltd.

ISBN 0 85973 025 5

First published in Great Britain 1987
as a co-operative venture between Stam Press Ltd and the City and Guilds of London Institute.

Reprinted 1989

© Stam Press Ltd, Cheltenham, 1987.

Printed and bound in Great Britain by Martin's of Berwick.

Project Structure and Use of Syllabus Bank and Supporting Books

1   The TECHNOLOGY associated with a given industrial process is a common requirement, but the APPLICATIONS vary by occupation and task, so a distinction has to be made between:

    (a)   THE AIM of the process: eg. to bend, metals, to drill, etc.

    (b)   THE LEARNING and ASSESSMENT: related to the application(s) specific to the industry to which the candidate belongs or aspires, or to the context of scheme chosen as a basis of study.

2   The approach suggested for the learning and assessment of any process technology is as follows:

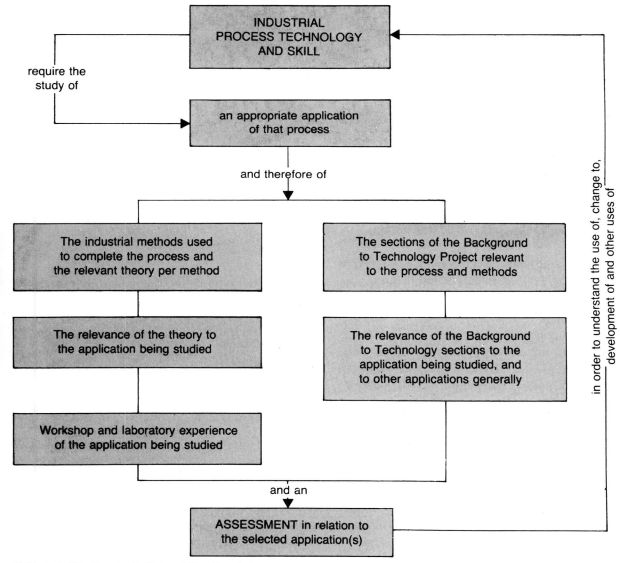

Fabrication of a large machine component, illustrating
positioning and locating for subsequent work

2.1 The definition and purpose of fabrication

A fabrication can be defined as 'the construction and erection of engineering structures from sub-assemblies'.

The joining procedures most commonly used in a fabrication are welding, riveting and bolting.

Fabrications consist of a wide variety of engineering constructions ranging from air conditioning plant and ventilation trunking to large steel bridges. Figs. **2.1.**1 to **2.1.**4 show four typical fabrications, the construction of which requires competence in measurement, drawing interpretation, joining methods and movement of materials.

A combination of education, training and practical experience is essential to produce fabrications with accuracy, speed and safety. Indeed safety in construction and erection must be a primary consideration at all times (for example the movement of heavy, perhaps unbalanced, components presents hazards that must be recognised and guarded against).

Fig. **2.1.**2　Cement silos – site erection

Some general considerations

This book sets out to cover the essential ingredients of the fabrication process. Foremost of these are the need for sound planning of the total operation plus careful recognition of safety requirements and practices. To summarise in general terms, when carrying out fabrication work the following points should always be observed:

● Study the drawings and if possible a similar type of job. Determine the sequence of work, the equipment required, the location of parts and sub-assemblies and the tolerances allowed.

Fig. **2.1.**1　Radio telescope fabrication

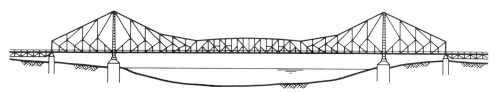

Fig. **2.1.**3　Cantilever bridge

Fig. **2.1.**4   Assembly through lifting of transhipment unit by marine equipment

● Determine the safety requirements, e.g. the type of protective clothing necessary, precautions against fire and what lifting equipment will be required.

● Proceed with the fabrication in the sequence that has been decided. Take particular care with dimensions measured from datum lines. Observe safe working practices at all times.

● Do not continue with the fabrication if in any doubt. It is better to consult with and ask advice from someone in authority rather than produce inferior work.

● On completion of the fabrication, study the method used, to consider whether improvements are possible if you are required to do similar work in the future.

Fabrication is carried out in stages, each of which requires careful consideration before work commences.

Here is a list of the stages which we shall consider in detail.

2.2. a–1 List of stages

- Preparation of the working area
- Movement of component parts, tools and equipment
- Determination of sequence of work
- Determination of the position and location of the different components to be joined
- Setting up
- Measuring and checking during setting up
- Fitting to size of the components to be joined
- Joining
- Holding, supporting and reinforcing during joining
- Checking the assembly dimensions, straightness and flatness
- Levelling and removal of distortion
- Finishing
- Inspection of completed fabrication to ensure that it is correct to drawing tolerances, is in accordance with specifications and is suitable for the function for which it is intended.

2.3 Preparation of the working area

2.3.a Floor space required

It is essential that the working area is inspected before the start of any fabrication work or the gathering together of the necessary materials, tools and equipment. The working drawings should be consulted to ascertain the floor area required for the assembly; it is as well to remember that the fabrication may need to be turned over during the assembly process and therefore the required working area may be larger than the dimensions entered on the drawings. An area for the storage of materials, tools and sub-assemblies must be allowed for.

2.3.b Availability of materials, tools and equipment

A variety of materials, tools and equipment is likely to be needed to complete the fabrication. These requirements must be assessed before work starts; they must be listed and obtained, in order that delays in the progress of the fabrication are avoided.
Determine what services are required and ensure that they are available for use during the fabrication, e.g. welding gases, compressed air for pneumatic tools, three-phase electricity supply for the larger electrical machinery and a single-phase electricity supply for small power tools and inspection lamps (110v a.c. preferred).

2.3.c Availability of the sub-assemblies

A fabrication sometimes consists of many sub-assemblies that might be manufactured away from the principal working area. These sub-assemblies should be delivered to the working area at the time when it is estimated that they will be required to be included in the fabrication. Late delivery of sub-assemblies will cause delay that may lead to an increase in the final costs.
Sub-assemblies if delivered too early can cause problems with storage and this situation, too, should be avoided.

2.3.d Lifting equipment

If the fabrication is likely to be heavy, consideration must be given to lifting it. Arrangements must be made to ensure that lifting equipment with adequate capacity is available at the work area.
All lifting equipment – cranes, jacks and blocks and tackle – has safe working load limits. It is essential, therefore, that the weights that are to be supported should be correctly estimated and that the weights are within the limits of the safe working loads of the lifting equipment.
If cranes are to be used, consideration must be given to the need for headroom and arc of travel. It is essential to ensure that all lifting equipment can be manoeuvred freely about the working area.

2.3.e Security of materials, tools and equipment

A site where a large fabrication is being erected is sometimes difficult to oversee; arrangements should be made to ensure that attractive items of material, such as tools and equipment, are kept in a secure area.
Provision must also be made to protect any material and equipment liable to be damaged if it is left exposed to the elements.

2.4 Transport of component parts of the fabrication

The safe movement of sub-assemblies, assemblies and equipment about the working area must receive major consideration. Where large fabrications are in progress, e.g. bridge building, an integrated transportation system with one-way traffic flow, traffic signals and controls might be introduced. Smaller fabrications also require that the movement of materials is adequately planned.

2.4.a Modes of transport

The following methods for the transport and lifting of materials about the working area are used:

- **Manual** – limited to components not weighing more than 20 kg
- **Handcart** – used for the movement of quantities of small components, any one of which will not weigh more than 20 kg
- **Forklift** – used for the transport of heavy but relatively small bulk items

Details of these methods can be obtained from the series book *Observing Safe Practices and Moving Loads*. Other handling and lifting equipment includes:

- **Hand or mechanised pulley blocks** (Fig. **2.4.**1a,b)
- **Derricks** (Fig. **2.4.**1c)
- **Gantries** (Fig. **2.4.**1g)
- **Tower cranes** (Fig. **2.4.**1f)
- **Swivel head cranes** (Fig. **2.4.**1d)
- **Floating cranes**
- **Special-to-type structures**.

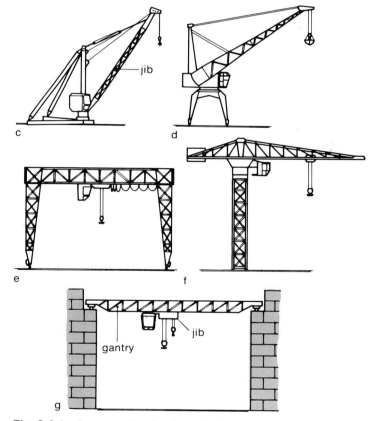

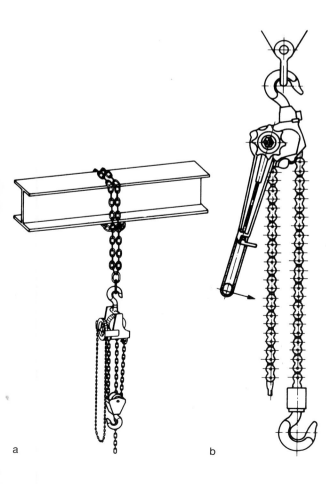

Fig. **2.4.**1   Some methods of mechanical lifting – cranes

a   A manually operated chain and pulley block
b   A ratchet operated pulley block
c   Derrick
d   Wharf crane (swivel head)
e   Goliath crane (outdoor travelling)
f   Tower crane
g   Overhead travelling crane (indoor workshop)

2.4.b Planning the movement, lifting and security of a load

The several sub-assemblies of the fabrication need to be brought together for final assembly. Large loads may be involved and to move these will require careful planning. When a load is to be moved about the working area the method to be employed must be decided as listed in Paragraph **2.4.a.** A combination of methods may be necessary. A crane or pulley block may be needed first to lift the load and place it on a forklift, which will be used to move the load across the site, to where another crane will lift the load from the forklift before it can finally be placed in the required position.

Irrespective of how the movement is to be achieved, the following points must be observed:

- **Establish the weight of the load.** Determine the position of the centre of gravity, select the correct lifting equipment and accessories, secure the load by attaching to points which are strong enough and will give a balanced lift (Fig. **2.4.**2a).

- **Check security.** Operate the lifting equipment until the load is about to be raised, then ascertain that all accessories are fitting correctly, e.g. that hooks and clamps are correctly seated and chains or ropes not twisted or knotted. Make sure that all persons are clear and then lift the load just clear of the surface, to ensure that it is balanced and will not swing sideways when lifted.

- **Lifting.** Check that balance is maintained; keep well clear of loads being raised; in no circumstances walk under a raised load. Never ride on a load (Fig. **2.4.**2b).

- **Horizontal moving.** The path of movement must be clear of obstructions. Loads must **never** be transported over personnel (Fig. **2.4.**2c). If the load is likely to swing during travel a guide rope should be used (Fig. **2.4.**2d).

- **Lowering.** This should be done slowly to avoid damage to the fabrication or the floor surface. Chocks should be placed to avoid trapping and assist in the removal of lifting accessories (see Paragraph **2.4.**h).

- **Examination of equipment.** After the lifting accessories have been removed they must be checked for damage, cleaned and returned to the correct storage place. Any damaged equipment must be reported and arrangements made for repair or replacement.

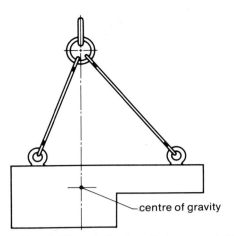

a Use of different sling lengths to ensure balance

b Never ride on a load

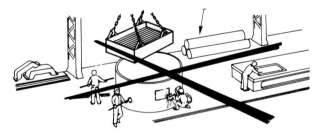

c Never direct a load over people

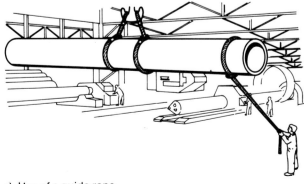

d Use of a guide rope

Fig. **2.4.**2 Safety factors relating to load movement

2.4.c Lifting accessories

In the majority of cases lifting equipment includes accessories used for specific tasks. These accessories must always be kept in a clean and safe condition; cleanliness is emphasised, since unless the equipment is kept in a clean condition any damage will be difficult to detect.

- **Crane hooks:** These hooks, especially those used for heavy loads, are usually suspended in a block which enables them to swivel in any direction (Fig. 2.4.3 a-c). An auxiliary hook must be fitted to the main chain hook if the ring or rings of the chain do not seat in the bottom of the hook (Fig. 2.4.3 d–e).

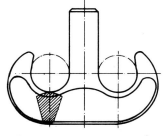

c Double crane hook for heavy loads

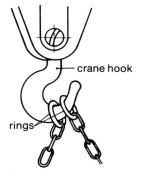

d Danger – rings not properly seated

a Crane hook for light (small) loads

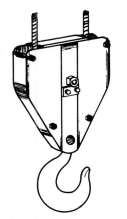

b Crane hook for medium loads

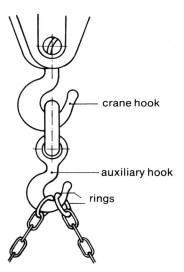

e Safety – auxiliary hook fitted: rings seated securely

Fig. **2.4.3**   Crane hooks

- **Chains:** Steel chains (Fig. 2.4.4) are manufactured using specialised equipment and welding processes. The most common assemblies are:
  two-hook chains: used to lift easily balanced loads in conjunction with eyenuts or eyebolts and rectangular plates with suitable plate clamps (Fig. 2.4.4a).
  three-hook chains: used to lift unbalanced loads or round plates. Eyenuts, eyebolts or plate clamps are fitted to the load (Fig. 2.4.4b).

chain sling with two lifting eyes: used to lift sections or for the suspension of pulley blocks (Fig. 2.4.4c).
When a chain is used for lifting loads with sharp edges the link formation takes up a favourable position relative to the edges of the load and links are rarely cut or damaged. However, chains are often severely damaged when knotted and trapped under the load. To prevent this happening care must be exercised when positioning the chain.

Chocks should be placed in position beneath the load to provide sufficient clearance to allow free movement of the chain after release.

Care and safety note: Oil regularly to prevent rusting. Examine before and after use for crushed and damaged links. The repair of links is a specialised job. **Do not attempt to self weld cracked links:** Special processes are necessary, e.g. atomic hydrogen and flash butt welding.

- **Steel wire slings.** These are available in a variety of diameters and lengths and have spliced loops at either end (Fig. **2.4.5a**). The loops are often provided with steel liners, the splice being formed about an aluminium ferrule. Examine wire ropes for broken strands, crushing and kinking. Wire ropes have lubricant introduced during manufacture. Rusting is a sign that the internal lubricant has been exhausted and the rope is likely to be weak. Wire ropes should be stored away from heat, steam and weather. Wire ropes must not be used to lift hot materials or be slung round corners that will cause the rope to bend to a radius less than three times the rope diameter.

Sharp corners should be covered with special timber packings or, if these are not available, sections from old tyres (Fig. **2.4.5c**).

- **Fibre rope slings.** These are also available in a variety of diameters and lengths with spliced eyes at the ends (Fig. **2.4.5b**).

Care and safety note. Fibre ropes are affected by damp, heat, oils, acids or chemicals. Sharp corners should be protected as shown in Fig. **2.4.5d**.

eyebolt

a Two-hook chain used for lifting fabrication with eyebolts

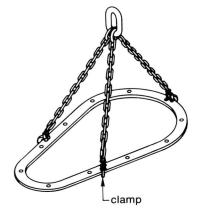

b Three-hook chains lifting a plate, using clamps

clamp

Fig. **2.4.4** Use of lifting chains

c Chain with two lifting eyes

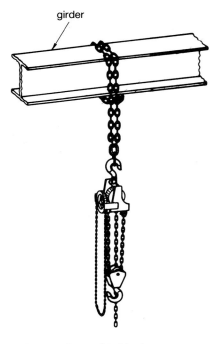

girder

d Suspending pulley blocks

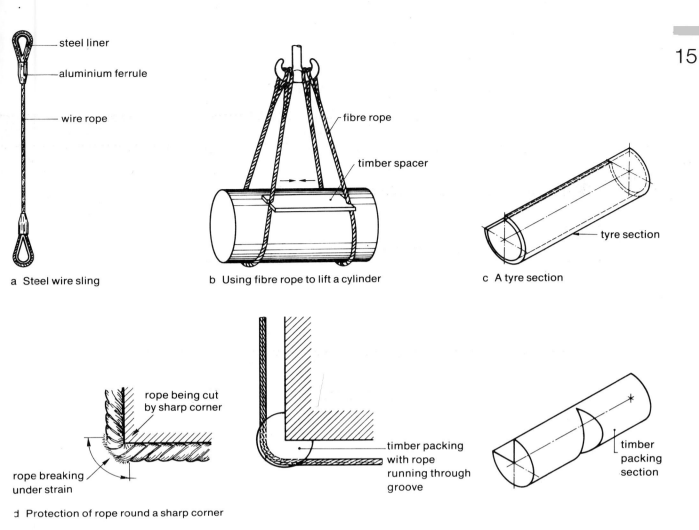

a Steel wire sling

- steel liner
- aluminium ferrule
- wire rope

b Using fibre rope to lift a cylinder

fibre rope

timber spacer

c A tyre section

tyre section

rope being cut by sharp corner

rope breaking under strain

timber packing with rope running through groove

timber packing section

d Protection of rope round a sharp corner

Fig. **2.4.**5   Lifting by steel and fibre ropes

Fig. **2.4.**6   Use of fibre and steel ropes (lifting a crankshaft)

Fig. **2.4.**6 shows wire and fibre ropes being used to lift a large crankshaft.

- **Shackles.** The shackles shown in Fig. **2.4.**7 are used to connect lengths of chain or for lifting fabrications by attaching eyebolts or eyenuts.

The lifting shackles illustrated are fitted in pairs or fours to lugs attached to fabrications.

The bolts supplied with the shackles are made from special steel and must not be replaced by bolts of different types.

It is important that when a shackle is fitted over a lug there is a close fit to prevent any tilting. If necessary, pads should be welded to the lug to ensure a good fit (Fig. **2.4.**8).

a Incorrect fitting (shackle can tilt)

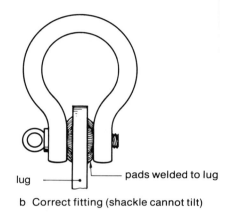

b Correct fitting (shackle cannot tilt)

Fig. **2.4.**8 Fitting of shackles

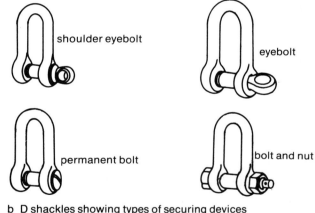

b D shackles showing types of securing devices

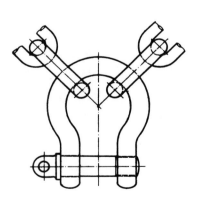

a Lifting shackles

Fig. **2.4.**7 Shackles

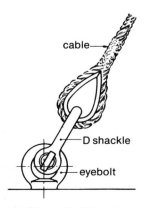

c Lifting with D shackle and eyebolt

- **Lifting beams.** Long plates and long flimsy fabrications present problems when they are lifted or moved because they are easily distorted. They should be lifted with a lifting beam (Fig. **2.4.**9). As can be seen, the beam serves to distribute the stresses imposed by the lifting forces.

- **Plate clamps.** Different types of plate clamps used for vertical lifting or the turning of plates are shown in Fig. **2.4.**10. When in use the plate must fully enter the throat of the clamp. In order that the clamps may be released safely, chocks must be placed beneath the load to support the weight.

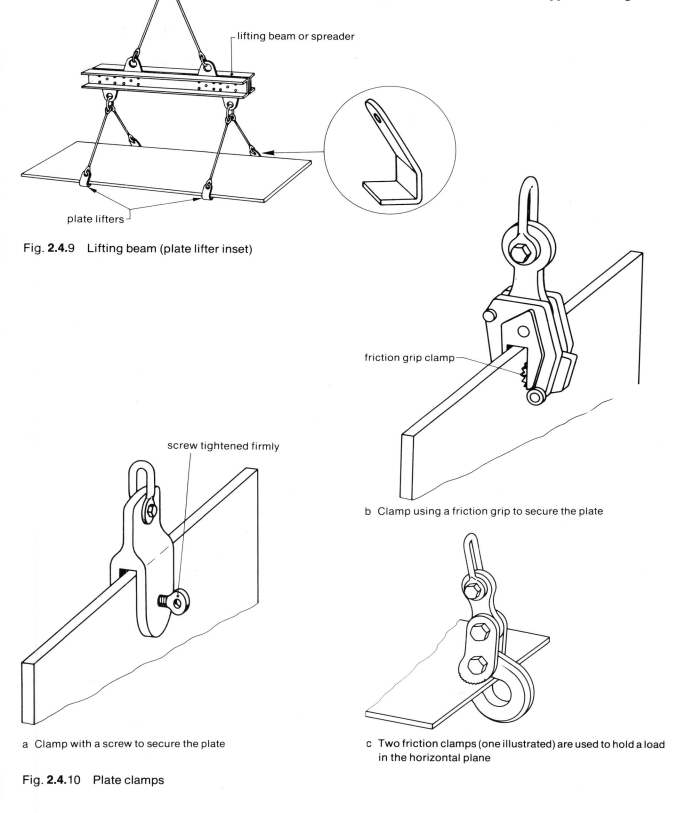

Fig. **2.4.**9 Lifting beam (plate lifter inset)

lifting beam or spreader

plate lifters

friction grip clamp

b Clamp using a friction grip to secure the plate

screw tightened firmly

a Clamp with a screw to secure the plate

c Two friction clamps (one illustrated) are used to hold a load in the horizontal plane

Fig. **2.4.**10 Plate clamps

2.4.d Materials used in the manufacture of lifting accessories

The common lifting accessories and a short explanation of their construction are given below.

- **Chains** are made from high tensile steel, but some older types of wrought iron or mild steel chains are still in service. The older type of chain is necessarily of heavier construction to provide the same strength; such chains require annealing every year.
- **Steel wire slings** are constructed from high tensile steel wire; the strength depends on the diameter of the wire, number of strands and the core. Grease is inserted during manufacture.
- **Rope slings** are made from natural hemp or nylon. A special type of sling consists of rope wound on to a steel core.
- **Crane hooks, shackles and lifting eyes** are made from forged steel.
- **Lifting beams** are fabricated from structural steel. The fabrication should be stress relieved and certified for the safe working load.
- **Plate lifters** must be hot forged and not cold bent. They should be crack detected and certified for the safe working load.

Care and safety note. It is essential that when a load is to be lifted the person responsible for the operation is satisfied that it is safe to use the available lifting equipment.

2.4.e Safe working load

Table **2.4.**1 shows typical safe working loads for steel wire ropes, fibre ropes and short-link chains.

All lifting accessories are governed by the Factories Act. Tables of safe loads must be posted in the stores and elsewhere, but these need not cover any equipment which has the safe working load clearly marked on it. Chains, ropes and other lifting tackle in use must be examined by a competent authority at regular intervals of not more than six months. A register of all lifting accessories must be kept. Except for fibre ropes and slings, lifting tackle must not be taken into use for the first time until it has been tested and certified.

Care and safety note. Check the safe working load of any lifting accessory before use by examining the stampings or metal tabs on the equipment. In the absence of these consult the tables in the stores. Values may be different from those given in Table **2.4.**1 owing to different materials and construction.

2.4.f Applications of equipment and accessories for the vertical and horizontal movement of loads

The equipment can be divided into three groups:
- That used to provide for vertical movement over short distance (low lifts)
- That used to provide for lifting to greater heights (high lifts)
- That used to provide for horizontal movement.

2.4.f.i Equipment for low lifts

It is not always possible to lift from above, using a crane or pulley block. Where space is limited it might be necessary to apply the lifting force from below or from the side of the load. Some equipment used in these tasks is listed below:

- **Crowbars** are used for temporary lifting when it is sufficient for muscle power to be augmented by a lever (Fig. **2.4.**11a).
- **Screwjacks** are often used in tandem to lift heavy fabrications steadily and evenly to the required level (Fig. **2.4.**11b). An example of the principle involved is the levelling screws on a set of scales.
- **Hydraulic jacks** provide a faster lifting method than screwjacks, but are more expensive (Fig. **2.4.**11c). They are, however, more economical to use, since the load can be rapidly raised to the required position.

It is essential to make sure that the floor is suitable for supporting the loaded jack and that jacking points are sufficiently robust; thick plates should

a Crowbar

Fig. **2.4.**11 Equipment used for low lifts (continued on page 20)

Table 2.4.1 Maximum loads for slings made from steel wire rope, fibre ropes and short-link chains under various load conditions.

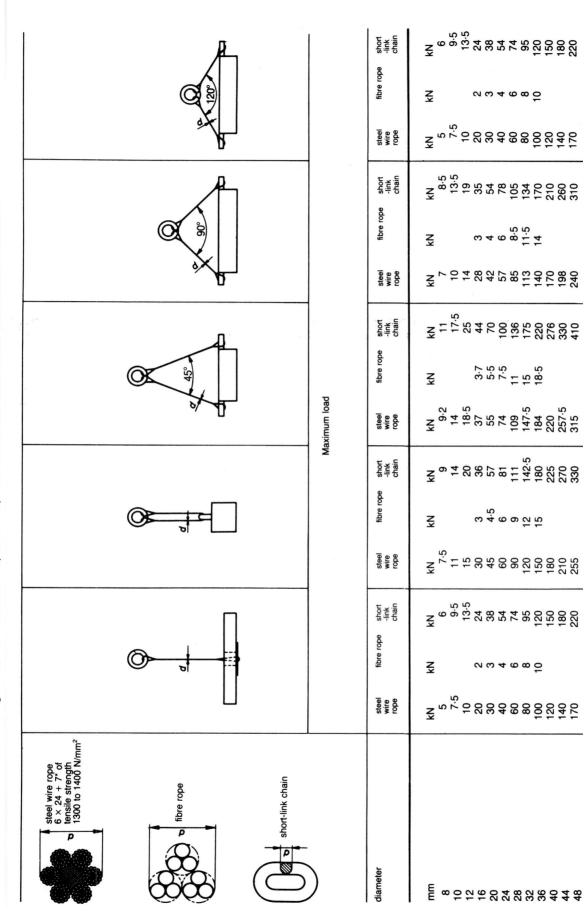

steel wire rope 6 × 24 + 7* of tensile strength 1300 to 1400 N/mm²

fibre rope

short-link chain

Maximum load

diameter	steel wire rope	fibre rope	short-link chain	steel wire rope	fibre rope	short-link chain	steel wire rope	fibre rope	short-link chain	steel wire rope	fibre rope	short-link chain	steel wire rope	fibre rope	short-link chain
mm	kN	kN	kN	kN	kN	kN	kN	kN	kN	kN	kN	kN	kN	kN	kN
8	5		6	7.5		9	9.2		11	7		8.5	5		6
10	7.5		9.5	11		14	14		17.5	10		13.5	7.5		9.5
12	10	2	13.5	15	3	20	18.5	3.7	25	14	3	19	10	2	13.5
16	20	3	24	30	4.5	36	37	5.5	44	28	4	35	20	3	24
20	30	4	38	45	6	57	55	7.5	70	42	6	54	30	4	38
24	40	6	54	60	9	81	74	11	100	57	8.5	78	40	6	54
28	60	8	74	90	12	111	109	15	136	85	11.5	105	60	8	74
32	80	10	95	120	15	142.5	147.5	18.5	175	113	14	134	80	10	95
36	100		120	150		180	184		220	140		170	100		120
40	120		150	180		225	220		276	170		210	120		150
44	140		180	210		270	257.5		330	198		260	140		180
48	170		220	255		330	315		410	240		310	170		220

*The figures quoted refer only io steel ropes of the 6 × 24 + 7 construction and of the quoted tensile strength.

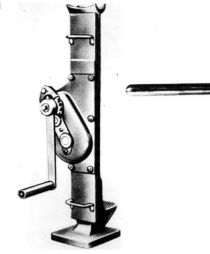

b Screwjacks

Fig. **2.4**.11   Equipment used for low lifts *(continued)*

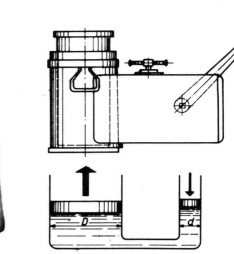

c Hydraulic jack (principle illustrated)

be used to spread the load. Jacks should be augmented by chocks if any work is to be carried out under the fabrication.

2.4.f.ii Equipment for high lifts

Rope, chain, steel cable. Each item has its specific use.

- **Ropes** are used to lift relatively light loads where chains or wire ropes would damage the surface, e.g. polished stainless steel, copper, aluminium or machined shafts.
- **Chains** are often preferred for workshop use as they are more durable than ropes or steel cables (Fig. **2.4**.12a).
- **Steel cables** (Fig. **2.4**.12b) are used where there is a need for flexibility to wrap round loads and for very high lifts on site, where the extra weight of chains, as compared with cables, is a disadvantage.

Cable sheaves: These provide a rapid method for lightweight parts, e.g. lifting the parts of light structural frames on site.

Pulley blocks: Pulley blocks and winches can be hand, electrically or pneumatically operated to provide portable lifting facilities on site and in the workshop (Figs. **2.4**.13 and **2.4**.14). Used on either single track gantries, swinging jib arms or a fixed anchor site in an overhead girder, they complement and can be used instead of the main workshop crane. **Care and safety note.** Select the attachment point for the cable sheaves and pulley block with care; if in any doubt about its strength consult the supervisor.

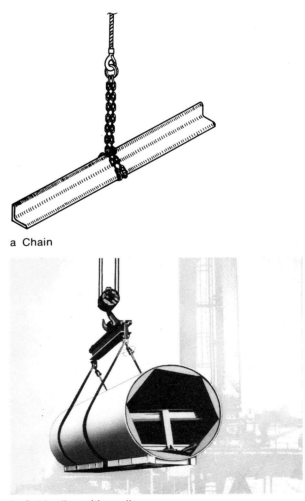

a Chain

b Cable sling with cradle

Fig. **2.4**.12   Equipment used for high lifts

2.4.f.iii Equipment for horizontal transportation

Forklift trucks are used for the transport of small heavy fabrications and equipment between workshops and within the workshop where headroom is limited.

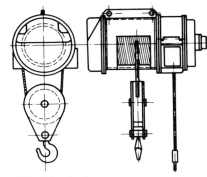

a Electric winch

a Chain pulley block   b Worm gear pulley block

Fig. **2.4.**13   Types of pulley block for high lifts

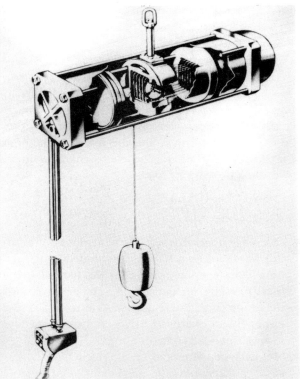

b Pneumatic winch

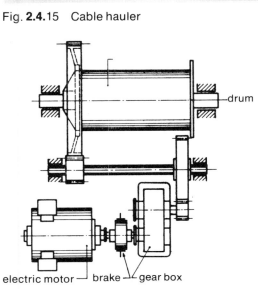

Fig. **2.4.**15   Cable hauler

Fig. **2.4.**14   High lift equipment – power winches

electric motor ⎯ brake ⏌⎯ gear box

a Electric winch

b Hand winch

Fig. **2.4.**16   Winches (for horizontal and vertical force)

Hauling blocks (Fig. **2.4.**15) and winches (Fig. **2.4.**16) are used where headroom is limited or where the roof structure cannot support a crane. Heavy fabrications laid on rollers or sledges are able to be hauled into position by using such equipment.

2.4.g Movement characteristics of cranes and derricks

The ability of a crane to move a load between two points on the same plane is dependent on the type of crane used. The movement characteristics of four types of crane are discussed below.

2.4.g.i Tower cranes

These are used on sites where very high lifts are required within a restricted area, e.g. a new building within a factory complex. Movement is limited to the radius of the jib arm round the tower of the crane (Fig. **2.4.**1f). The greater the extension of the jib, the lower the safe working load.

2.4.g.ii Travelling cranes

- **Overhead on gantries.** Movement along and across the workshop in a rectangle bounded by the rails on which the crane travels enables the full area of the workshop, or outside area, to be covered by the crane (Fig. **2.4.**1e and g). Control is achieved either by an overhead driver or from floor level using suspended controls.
- **Mobile type.** Mounted on a vehicle chassis, they have a freedom of movement that enables materials and equipment to be transported and positioned over a wide area on large sites, provided that hardstanding is available. When a mobile crane is travelling with a suspended load, great care must be taken to ensure that the load is always under control.

2.4.g.iii Floating cranes

Where the only access to a site is by water, floating cranes provide manoeuvrable lifting facilities. They are used extensively when carrying out repairs to ships' superstructures and harbour installations.

2.4.g.iv Derricks

Movement of material is limited to the radius of the jib arm around the winch (Fig. **2.4.**1c). The higher the elevation of the jib arm the greater the load which can be raised.

Increased mobility for tower cranes and derricks can be attained by having them mounted on bogies for use on rail tracks.

Safe practices

- **Signals to crane drivers:** It is most important that standard hand signals are used to convey instructions to crane drivers. It is equally vital that such signals are instantly understood. Even with the introduction of radio communication between the crane driver and the person requiring a load to be moved it is essential that the standard signals are understood, if only as insurance against a failure in the radio link. Fig. **2.4.**17 illustrates the hand signals that should be used.
- **Safe working loads.** These must be checked before using any equipment for lifting.
- **Defects.** These, however slight, must be reported to the supervisor.

Use only the proper signals to crane drivers

Fig. **2.4.**17   Standard signals to crane driver

2.4.h Chocking

2.4.h.i The purpose of chocking

Fig. **2.4.**18 shows the correct and incorrect methods of using chocks to stack material. This procedure:

- creates space between the floor and material to facilitate attachment and removal of lifting accessories
- enables materials and components to be safely stacked

- makes the parts accessible for future operations
- prevents movement where the contact area between the component and the surface on to which it is placed is insufficient for friction to overcome the tendency of the component to move, i.e. roll or slide. Chocking is also used to give side support to a component that is likely to become unbalanced.

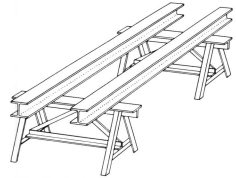

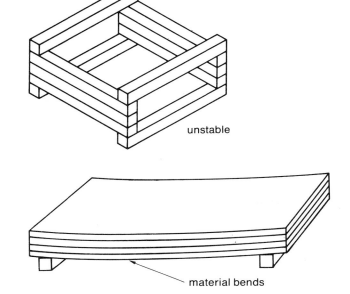

unstable

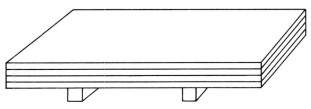

a Correct method

material bends

b Incorrect methods

Fig. **2.4.**18 Chocking

a Trestle stand

2.4.h.ii Accessories used in chocking

The following items are commonly used to ensure safe chocking:

- wood in standard dimensions, e.g. 100 mm × 100 mm, 200 mm × 200 mm, etc.
- pallets
- trestles and stands (Fig. **2.4.**19a)
- assembly floors constructed from rolled steel section (Fig. **2.4.**19b)
- combinations of the above.

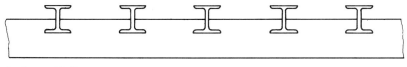

b Assembly floor

Fig. **2.4.**19 Trestle stand and assembly floor

2.5 Determining the work sequence

When any fabrication is to be produced there needs to be an overall plan or procedure to be followed if the result is to be satisfactory. Listed below are important factors that determine the sequence of work:
- preparation and collection of material
- marking out and cutting of material
- forming of material
- positioning and location of components
- accessibility of parts to be installed later
- accessibility for next operation
- available floor space and height
- the simplest and most economic method of working by considering the following factors:
  - i dimensions of the working area and nature of operations
  - ii equipment available
  - iii transport considerations
  - iv facilities for assembly at site.

A study of some simple fabrications will help to give a better understanding of the factors just listed. We shall start with the fabrication of the pressure vessel shown in Fig. **2.5**.1. The flow chart in Fig. **2.5**.2 suggests the sequences and procedures most likely to be followed in its manufacture.

Note: Paragraphs 2.5a, 2.5b, 2.5c and to some extent 2.5d refer generally to the pressure vessel, the subject of the flow chart in Fig. **2.5**.2.

2.5.a Preparation and collection of material

For the work to progress efficiently there should be a planned approach.

The preparation and collection of materials must be in accordance with the production plan.

Little work can be carried out until the pressed ends are received and exact diameters determined for the rolled cylinder and top and bottom flanges.

Fig. **2.5**.1   Vessel

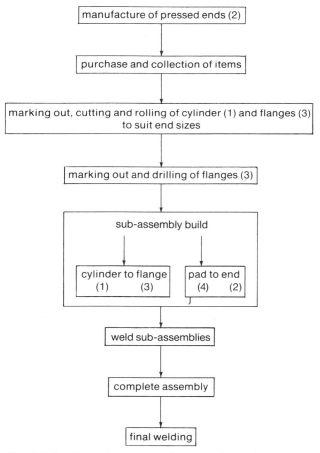

Fig. **2.5**.2   Flow chart – manufacture of vessel shown in Fig. **2.5**.1

2.5.b Marking out and cutting of material

These operations should provide the fabricator with datum lines or datum edges to assist in accurate and rapid assembly (refer to the series book *Measuring and Marking Out* for a full description). Note that:
- centre lines marked on the cylinder before rolling, on the pressed ends and on the flanges will make it easier to locate parts quickly
- the accurate pre-cutting of weld preparations and holes is essential.

2.5.c Forming of material

The forming operations used in the manufacture of the pressure vessel are:
- hot pressing of the end
- rolling of the body cylinder
- rolling of the flange rings.

There will probably be a difference in the sizes of the hot pressings as a result of contraction when cooling. This is the reason why hot pressing is the first in the sequence. Accurate rolling to suit the pressings can then be achieved.

2.5.d Positioning and location of components

The positive location of components on the pressure vessel is a progressive sequence, based on the use of a pre-marked centre line as a datum. Provided that continuous and accurate checks on squareness and dimensions are carried out during fabrication then no difficulties should be encountered.

The correct sequence of positioning and location ensures that rectification work will not be necessary on the completed fabrication.

Fig. **2.5.**3 shows a further example, a beam on which two double bearing blocks, X and Y, have to be installed and two structural members attached across the beam. The bearings have to be aligned to accept a shaft which must pass through the structural members.

One method for positioning the parts correctly involves measurement and the use of squares in the following sequence:
- attach the structural members to the beam and weld in position
- fix the bearings to the base
- thread the shaft through the bearings and structural members.

An alternative method would be to:
- thread the shaft through one pair of bearings, then through the structural members and then through the second pair of bearings
- fix the bearings to the beam
- attach the structural members and weld them in position.

If the two methods are examined it will be seen that the alternative (second) method should be chosen because the holes in the structural members and bearings would be certain to be in alignment, whereas in the first method the parts may be found to be out of alignment when the shaft is threaded through. This would result in costly rectification work.

Where possible the sequence must ensure correct positioning and location before final fixing.

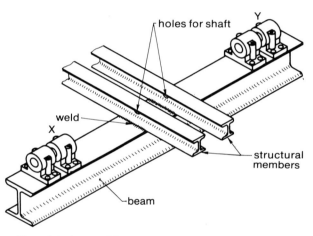

a Completed assembly

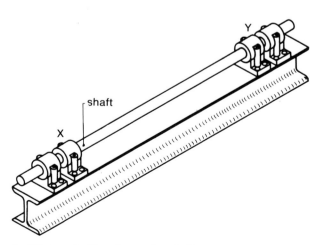

b Alignment of bearings using shaft

Fig. **2.5.**3 Illustration of positioning and location of parts

2.5.e Accessibility of parts to be installed later

In the example shown in Fig. **2.5.**4a, deflector baffles are to be fitted into a duct corner to minimise turbulence. Gaining access to fit the baffles might be difficult and two other procedures might be attempted.

- One would be to manufacture the duct corner complete and then insert and secure the corner baffle, followed by the centre baffle. Difficulties would be encountered when attempting this method, as small inaccuracies or any distortion would make it difficult for the baffles to be positioned without jamming.
- An alternative method would be to assemble the duct corner without the front plate, but fit temporary supports as shown in Fig. **2.5.**4b. The baffles can then be positioned and secured with ease. Finally the temporary supports would be removed and the front plate installed and secured.

2.5.f Accessibility for next operation

Fig. **2.5.**5 shows the cross section of a cylindrical drum. Since the bosses in the ends require welding both inside and outside it is impossible to complete the assembly and then carry out the welding. The following flow chart illustrates the manufacturing sequence that should be followed in this case.

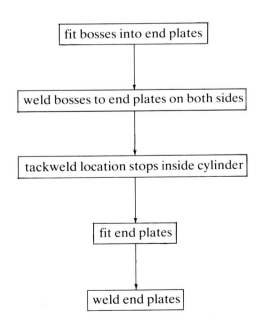

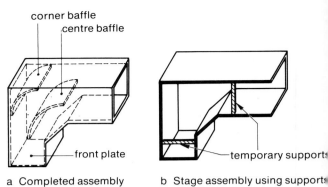

a Completed assembly   b Stage assembly using supports

Fig. **2.5.**4   Duct corner assembly

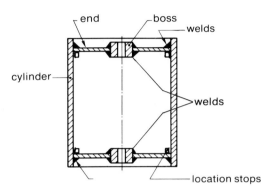

Fig. **2.5.**5   Cross section of cylindrical drum

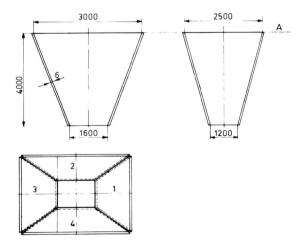

Fig. **2.5.**6   Bottom section of hopper

2.5.g Available floor space and height

The bottom section of the hopper shown in Fig. **2.5.**6 is to be assembled.

The preferred method of assembly is on the connection face A. The smallest possible shop-floor area will be used, but the greatest crane height for lifting sides 1 and 3 into position will be needed as these sides are 4.06 m long. When lifting the final assembly using a two-hook chain a clearance of approximately 6.6 m to the crane hook will be necessary. The assembly sequence will be:

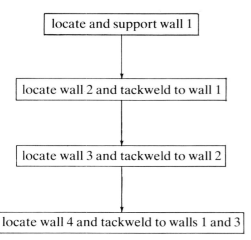

If the necessary crane height was not available the method of assembly using the smallest crane height with the largest shop-floor area would be in the following sequence:

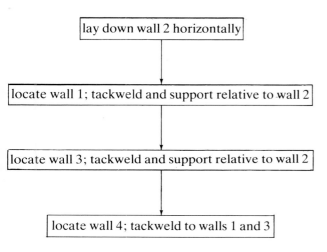

The second method will present greater difficulties in ensuring that both ends are square and level.

2.5.h Prefabrication

Fabrications have to be studied to consider the simplest and most economical method of working. This usually involves the prefabrication of sub-assemblies for final assembly, either in the workshop or at the installation site.

A combination of the following factors is usually involved.

2.5.h.i Dimensions of the working area and the nature of operations

Fabrications may be too large for the working area. Moreover it is not economical for one fabrication to occupy a large area of shop-floor if this prevents work continuing on other fabrications. In this case prefabrication in a number of sections for final assembly at the installation site is usual.

Fig. **2.5**.7 shows a butane storage tank which will occupy a large shop-floor area. By fabricating the tank in three sections with site welds at X, three teams of fabricators will be able to work independently, thereby making more efficient use of the shop-floor area.

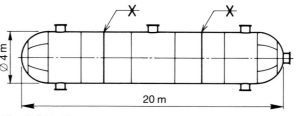

Fig. **2.5.7**   Butane storage tank: sectional fabrication

The requirements of on-site operations need consideration. Suitable power supplies for welding and large amounts of water for hydraulic testing are required. Safety measures need to be thoroughly examined, especially if the installation is to be carried out in an existing butane storage area.

2.5.h.ii The equipment available

The weight of the completed fabrication must not be greater than the safe working load of the lifting equipment. It is essential, therefore, that weights of all sub-assemblies should be calculated to ensure that the site lifting equipment can safely cope with the overall weight when assembled.

The requirement for machine tools must also be considered, since many fabrications need finishing operations using lathes, boring machines or milling machines.

If the flanges on the segment bend in the long pipe shown in Fig. **2.5**.8 require machining to provide

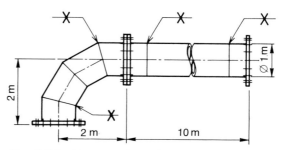

Fig. **2.5**.8   Segment bend in long pipe

good jointing faces a very large boring machine would be required. By welding short sections to the flanges and finally welding the seams marked X together after machining, the flanges could be machined on a simple centre lathe with a short bed.

Similar considerations of other fabrications can enable machining operations to be carried out on sub-assemblies using simple machine tools.

2.5.h.iii Transport considerations

The following points must be taken into consideration:
- Weight of load for lifting on site
- Width, height and length of load to be checked against the access route from within workshops to within site
- Flexibility of load and the likelihood of distortion, e.g. roof frame structures as shown in Fig. 2.5.9 are usually constructed from light angles and tees; these are often transported to the site in pieces for assembly.

Note. Competent transport contractors will usually be familiar with the route requirements regarding low bridges, weight limitations, restricted access, etc.

2.5.h.iv Facilities for assembly at the working site

To sum up the points already considered, the following facilities must be examined at the working site:
- Suitable services, e.g. electricity, water
- Access for materials and equipment
- Lifting facilities
- Health and Safety provisions in accordance with those required by the Factories Act.

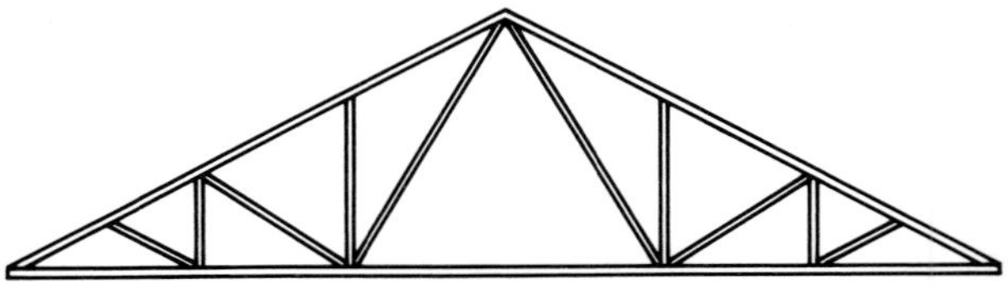

Fig. **2.5**.9   Roof frame structure

2.6 Locating parts to be joined

When any fabrication is assembled the component parts must be positioned accurately and positively before any permanent joints are made. The following points must be considered.

When fabricating a structure take extra care in the measuring, marking out and positioning of components. 'Think twice, cut once' is a good maxim to remember. A few extra minutes taken to ensure that the positioning is correct can save many hours of work and much expense in correcting faults which could arise from hurried and incorrect preparatory work.

2.6.a Determining position and location of parts

2.6.a.i–iv Use of marks, holes, datum lines, etc.

The following are used to position and locate components:

- drilled holes
- datum lines
- datum edges
- squared faces.

As an example Fig. **2.6.**1a shows two bolted or riveted connections on the type of roof frame shown in Fig. **2.5.**9.

The frame is assembled with the rafters and bottom tie forming a triangle. The plate gussets are fitted to these angles. Bracing angles are then fitted; as the long angles for the rafters and bottom tie will not be perfectly straight, location of the bracing angles is achieved by aligning the holes. This is done by hand leverage in the holes with a podger spanner or by hammering hardened steel taper drifts into the holes (Fig. **2.6.**1b and c).

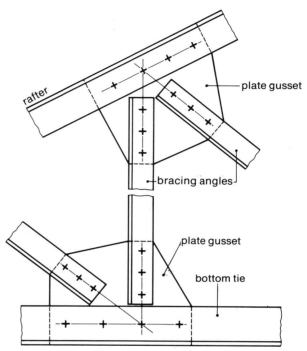

a Roof frame connections

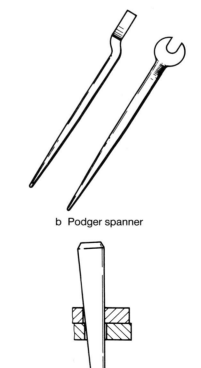

b Podger spanner

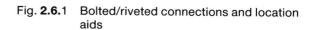

c Taper drift

Fig. **2.6.**1 Bolted/riveted connections and location aids

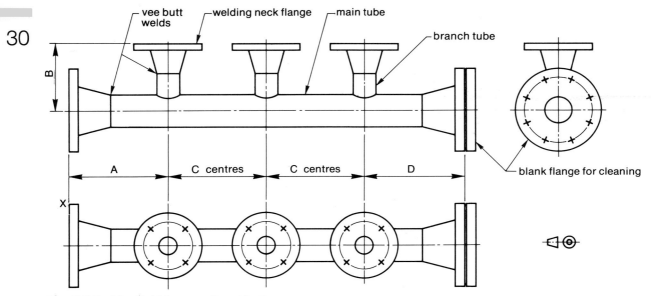

Fig. **2.6.**2 Manifold for a sectional boiler

Fig. **2.6.**2 shows a manifold for a sectional boiler. The branch connections need to be located at distance A from square datum face X with the centres C apart and with the faces in line at distance B from the centre line of the main tube.

The assembly sequence using centre lines and datum faces is:

1. Assemble three sub-assemblies consisting of the branch tubes and welding neck flanges.
2. Mount the main tube in vee blocks with the centre line of the pre-drilled holes at the top (Fig. **2.6.**3a). Clamp in position and check with a spirit level.
3. Fit flanges to each end with one centre line vertical. Tackweld in position, check overall length and dimension H. See Fig. **2.6.**3b.
4. Mark out a rigid length of bright bar and clamp three sub-assemblies as in Fig. **2.6.**3c.
5. Set packings as in Fig. **2.6.**3d, place set up branches in position, check with spirit level and tackweld in position.
6. After welding, check up from the datum lines for distortion.

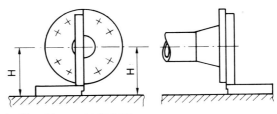

a Main tube set up

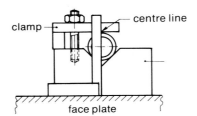

b Checking main flanges

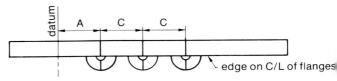

c Branches ready to fit

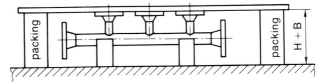

d Final set up

Fig. **2.6.**3 Manifold assembly sequence

2.6.b Using clamps, jigs and fixtures

For the rapid assembly of batches of fabrications the time-consuming operations of measurement from datum lines, centre lines and square faces and individual setting of parts are not economical. Jigs (Fig. **2.6**.4) and fixtures with work-holding devices (usually in the form of quick-acting clamps or magnets) can be used for rapid batch production. Two common types of clamp are cam action (Fig. **2.6**.5a) and toggle action (Fig. **2.6**.5b). Magnets are shown in Fig. **2.6**.6. The jig should:

- provide accurate location of the parts
- provide access for tackwelding or tackbolting
- permit easy removal of the assembly
- be sufficiently robust to prevent distortion, if the jig is to be kept in place whilst final welding is completed.

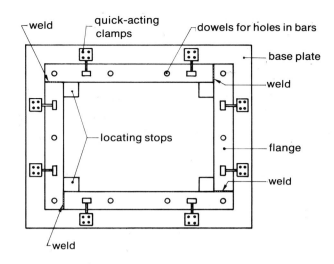

Fig. **2.6**.4   Jig for assembly of plat bar flanges

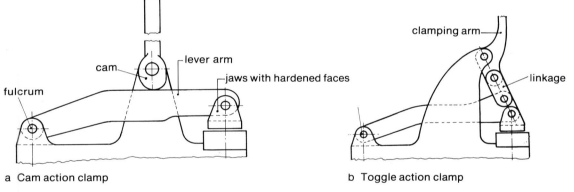

a Cam action clamp

b Toggle action clamp

Fig. **2.6**.5   Common clamps

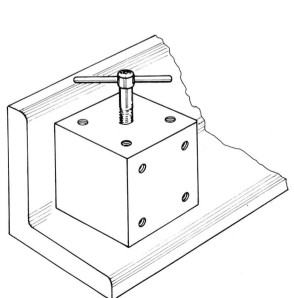

a Bar magnets

b Cube magnet holding angles

Fig. **2.6**.6   Types of magnet used in positioning

2.6.c Use of stops

Stops are used for accurate positioning of components to be welded. Fig. **2.6.**7 shows the assembly of angle bar stiffeners to a number of plates. To space the stiffeners equally and rapidly, four angle iron stops are manufactured equal in length to the gap between the stiffeners. By the use of magnets to locate the stops they do not need tackwelding and can be moved along progressively as the stiffeners are tackwelded in position.

2.6.d Stepping off from one part to another

If several identical assemblies are required, it is only necessary to mark out the first and then step off the others from it.

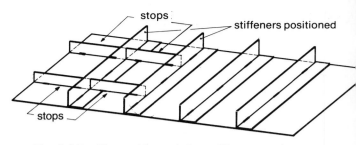

Fig. **2.6.**7   Plate with angle bar stiffeners and stops

Marking out during assembly is often required: the tools used are listed in the series book *Measuring and Marking Out*. Fig. **2.6.**8a shows a shaped plate with two lugs attached. If the first plate is marked out, points A, B, C and D may be transferred (Fig. **2.6.**8b) to the remainder, using dividers and odd-leg calipers. If a large number of identical parts is required the preparation of a sheet-metal template (Fig. **2.6.**8c) to act as a guide to marking out would be economical.

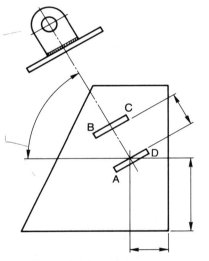

a Shaped plate with lugs

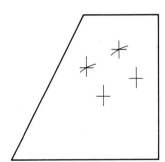

b Transferred points

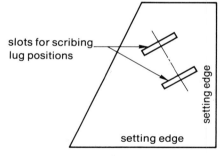

c Sheet-metal template

Fig. **2.6.**8   Illustration of a shaped plate, transferred points and a template

The process of setting up the parts to be joined entails the locating and positioning of the component parts of the fabrication to the assembly drawing specification before tackwelding or tackbolting.

2.7.a Classification

Assemblies can be classified into two groups for setting up procedures:
- **Thin plate and light sections.** These are fabrication components that are safely handled without the use of lifting apparatus.
- **Thick plate and rolled steel sections.** These are fabrication components that require the use of lifting apparatus for safe transportation and positioning.

2.7.b Typical tools used for thin plate and light sections

The tools and equipment for setting up thin plate and light sections should assist location without the need for excessive force. They include:
- grips, hammers, cramps, G clamps, wedges and magnets (Fig. **2.7**.1 and **2.7**.2)
- locating plates, cleats, braces, webs, perforated angles and corner struts (Fig. **2.7**.3).

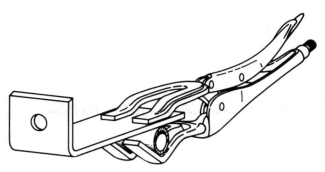

b Tube welding grips clamping pipe to bracket

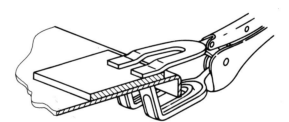

c Long reach welding grips clamping over flanged edge

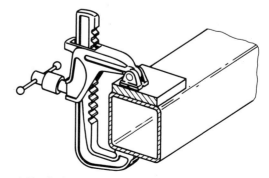

d Rack clamp clamps pad to hollow section

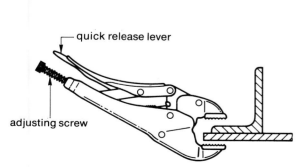

a Parallel jaw grips stiffener to plate edge

Fig. **2.7**.1 Use of typical clamps

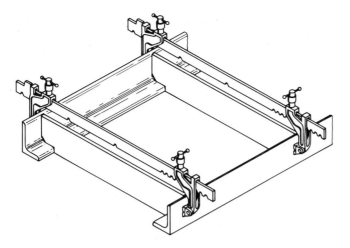

a Standard duty bar clamp
  Fitting cross bracing in angle frame

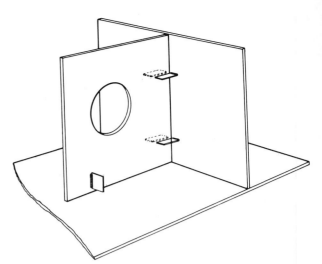

a Locating plates for setting up a partition

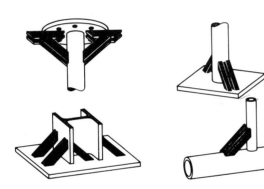

b Use of magnets for simple setting up

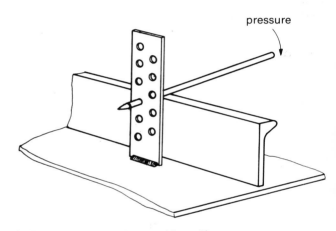

pressure

b Perforated angle plate used for setting up

c Clamp for positioning pipes at right angles

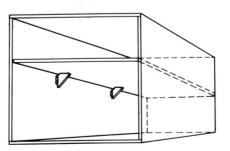

c Locating gussets for setting a vane in a duct

Fig. **2.7.**2   Uses of bar clamp, magnet and angle clamp

Fig. **2.7.**3   Locating devices

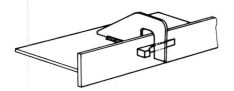

d Clamping cleat with wedge

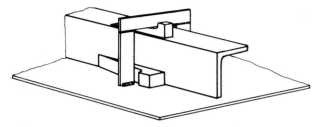

e Light bridge fixture using wedges for horizontal and vertical positioning

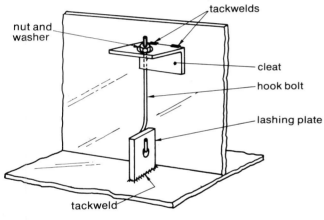

f Setting up partition for fillet welds

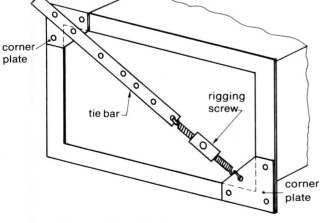

g Squaring up a flanged duct

Fig. **2.7**.3 Locating devices *(continued)*

The tools and equipment for setting up thick plate and rolled steel sections provide location and if necessary a large amount of force. They include:

● sledge hammers, ratchet pulley blocks, push-pull screws, screwjacks, hydraulic jacks, gas torches and wedges (Fig. **2.7**.4)

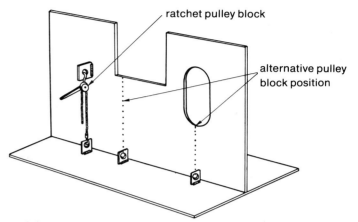

a Setting up a heavy divider plate using lashing plates and ratchet pulley block

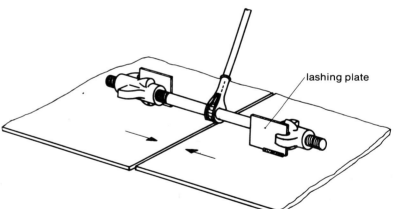

b Setting up using lashing plates and a push and pull screw

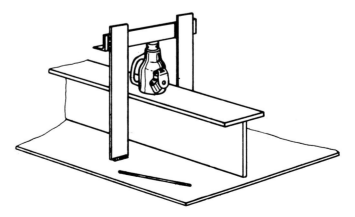

c Setting up using a bridge fixture and hydraulic jack

Fig. **2.7**.4   Typical tools for heavy section location

- cleats, lashing plates, wedge cleats, form cleats, clamping cleats and strongback (Fig. **2.7**.5 and **2.7**.6).

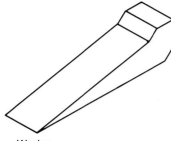

a Wedge

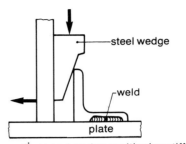

a Cleat and wedge positioning stiffener

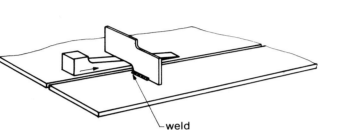

b Wedge cleat for aligning plates

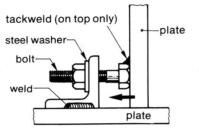

b Cleat and bolt positioning stiffener

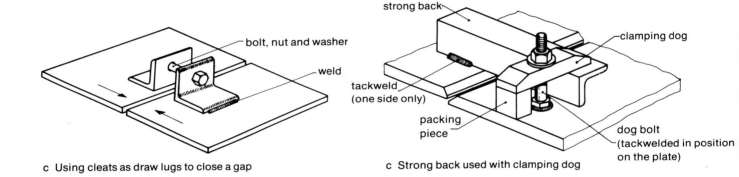

c Using cleats as draw lugs to close a gap

c Strong back used with clamping dog

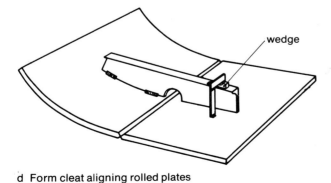

d Form cleat aligning rolled plates

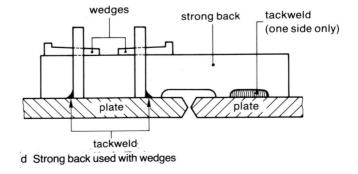

d Strong back used with wedges

Fig. **2.7**.5   Equipment for heavy duty location

Fig. **2.7**.6   Positioning stiffener and use of strong back

2.7.d The setting up of butt welded joints

Where two components are to be joined by welding the dimension of the gap between the edges must be that needed to ensure the correct amount of penetration. In some cases a gap is not acceptable and would be detrimental to the completed weld.

Fig. **2.7.7** shows the method of indicating welds on drawings, and the edge preparation required, using symbols as in BS 499. Incorrect weld fit-up can result in various defects (Fig. **2.7.8**), cause excessive consumption of electrodes, distortion and the need for undue back gouging. Welding defects can be detected by X-ray examination; typical samples of radiographs are shown in Fig. **2.7.**9.

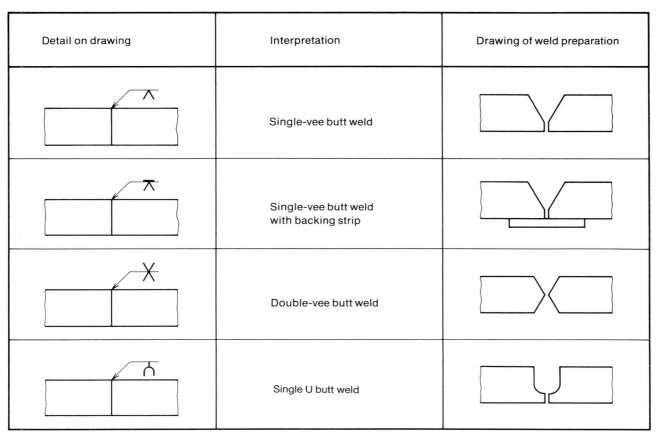

Detail on drawing	Interpretation	Drawing of weld preparation
	Single-vee butt weld	
	Single-vee butt weld with backing strip	
	Double-vee butt weld	
	Single U butt weld	

Fig. **2.7.7**   Extract from BS.499

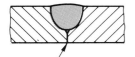
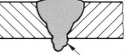
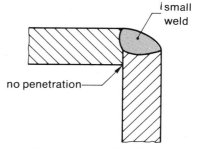
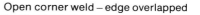

Vee butt weld — no gap

Vee butt weld — excessive gap

Open corner weld — edge overlapped

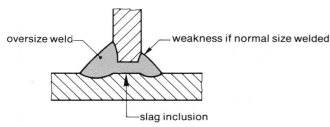
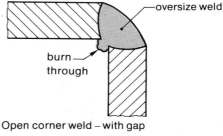

Tee fillets if gap left between plates

Open corner weld — with gap

Fig. **2.7.8**   Illustration of weld defects caused by incorrect fit-up

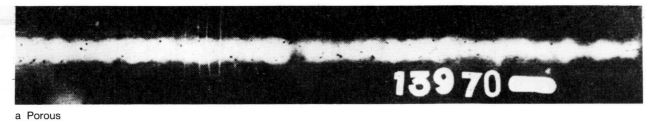

a Porous

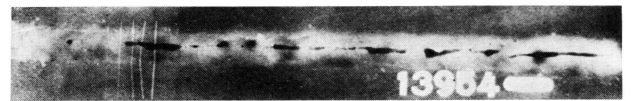

b Slag included

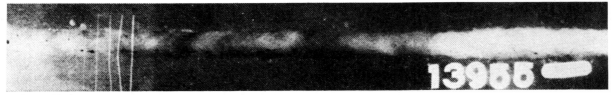

c Lack of fusion

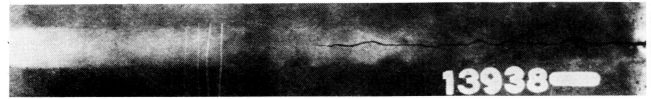

d Crack

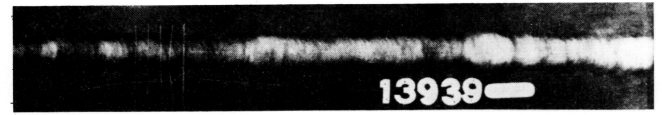

e Serration

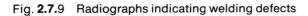

Fig. **2.7.**9   Radiographs indicating welding defects

Tackwelding and removal of cleats, lashing plates, etc.

Tackwelds should always be positioned so that they are easily accessible for weakening by chiselling or grinding, to assist removal by hammering or levering. Any temporary attachment, such as a lashing plate, should be capable of being removed without the parent plate sustaining damage. The plate surface should be ground flush, but not overground. Attachments should be cleaned and stored for future use.

The choice of tools and equipment for setting up

This depends upon the thickness of the material and the type of assembly. Assemblies using unstressed parts, such as plates and structural sections which have been cut to size and drilled, can be set up using simple holding and clamping methods; on the other hand stressed components, such as rolled and bent plates or welded sub-assemblies, may need to have considerable force exerted in order to overcome deviations of form, squareness and roundness. These highly stressed components are encountered in the connection of lengths of ducting, container and pressure vessel assembly and in complicated fabrications.

Tools are available for special applications

The vacuum and electromagnetic lifters (Fig. **2.7.**10) are used for positioning plate edges relative to one another and also for reinforcing strips on flat plates and holding them down at the same time.

2.7.e Dimensional checking during assembly

Frequent measuring and checking is necessary during setting up and positioning. This ensures that as the work proceeds any errors will be discovered and rectified before the fitting of further parts is made difficult or the job has to be taken apart and re-assembled. Tools and equipment include:

- squares (for squareness and position)
- straight edges (for straightness and flatness)
- rules and tapes (for dimension)
- gauges (for checking gaps and clearance)
- measuring rods and length gauges (for spacing)
- spirit levels and plumb lines (for checking horizontal and vertical planes)
- piano wires and string lines (to check alignment).

Reference to the series book *Measuring and Marking Out* is recommended.

a Vacuum lifter

b Electromagnetic lifter

Fig. **2.7.**10   Special tools for setting up

2.8 Fitting to size

2.8.a As a means of correcting deviations

This is the process of measuring, checking and adjustment to ensure that the component parts of a fabrication can be assembled correctly. Deviations occur as a result of inaccuracy

- arising from the accumulation of minor errors in marking out, cutting and forming of parts, especially those of complicated shape
- in the production of sub-assemblies
- in assembling the complete fabrication.

2.8.b Achieving the specification

Trial assembly will enable checks to be made to ensure that form, dimensions and function are in accordance with the drawings and/or specification.

2.8.c Methods of fitting to size

2.8.c.i–vii Methods available

- **filing** – to remove minor deviations, sharp edges and corners
- **chipping** – to remove slag from oxy-gas cut parts and welds
- **grinding** – to grind welds and any unwanted projections that obstruct the fit
- **cutting and trimming** – either by oxy-gas cutting or shearing
- **tackwelding** – it is sometimes necessary to tackweld a part in position so that it is held secure while holes to accommodate bolts or rivets are drilled accurately
- **selective assembly** – when a number of identical fabrications are required, in order to save time, parts which fit correctly can be selected from batches
- **bending and straightening** – to correct deviations in form and to correct distortion in sub-assemblies; this operation may be carried out hot or cold.

Example

Fig. **2.8.**1 shows a lightweight portal frame corner; the following fitting operations will need to be carried out during assembly.

Items 1 and 2 should be welded together as a sub-assembly. Before location in the assembly jig, the 90° angle between these parts must be checked and corrected. The weld should be ground flush locally to allow item 4 to seat in place. Before being fitted in the jig, item 3 will require the sharp edges, which were produced when the part was sheared to size, to be smoothed. Item 4 will have been cut on the oxy-gas template cutting machine. Slag should be chipped off before the item is trimmed to length to enable it to fit between items 1, 2 and 3 in the jig. Item 5 will need to have sharp edges filed off before checks are made for profile, after which it will be located in position. Trimming will probably be unnecessary. Items 5 and 6 may require setting to the exact profile of item 4 before assembly.

If a number of these fabrications are required, selective assembly should be used to avoid some fitting to size.

After welding, the completed fabrication should be refitted in the jig to check for form and dimensional accuracy. Some rectification of distortion on the column and beam mating faces is likely to be needed.

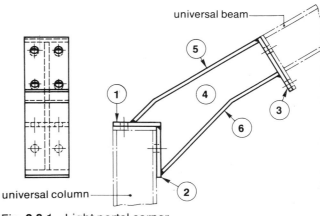

Fig. **2.8.**1   Light portal corner

2.9 Pre-setting and restraining during and after assembly

2.9.a Purpose of pre-setting and restraining

Distortion during welding is caused by the contraction of the molten weld pool and the effect of heat from the weld on the surrounding metal.

Pre-setting entails setting the parts so as to compensate for the movement of the material during the welding process. Such movement as occurs will, after pre-setting, bring the completed fabrication to the correct form and dimensions. Restraining controls the movement of components during subsequent operations.

Straightening and aligning afterwards is more difficult and costly than pre-setting and restraining.

Examples

- Fig. **2.9.**1a shows two plates set up for vee butt welding. If there is no restraint of pre-setting, distortion in both directions will result (Fig. **2.9.**1b).
- Fig. **2.9**1c shows a tee section set up for fillet welding.
- Fig. **2.9**1d shows the result of welding on one side.
- Fig. **2.9.**1e shows the result of a further weld on the second side. Longitudinal distortion will also take place as in Fig. **2.9.**1f.

Excessive distortion is caused by:

- gaps between set up parts
- oversize welds
- incorrect welding sequence.

These faults can be greatly reduced if those areas where distortion is more likely to occur are identified and the method of pre-setting or restraining can be decided in advance. This may need some discussion with the supervisor.

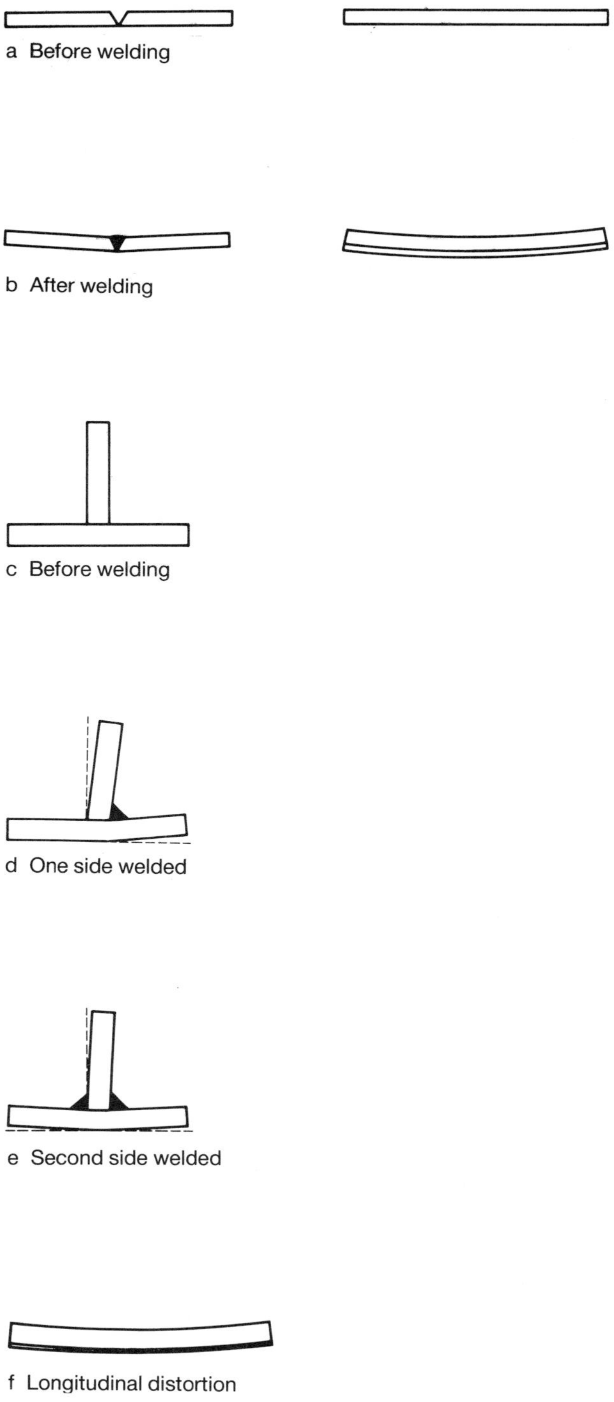

2.9.b Methods of restraint

2.9.b.i–iii Methods available

- arranging the sequence in which the parts are assembled and welded
- weighting or clamping
- using fixtures.

a Before welding

b After welding

c Before welding

d One side welded

e Second side welded

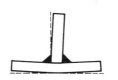

f Longitudinal distortion

Fig. **2.9.**1   Examples of distortion

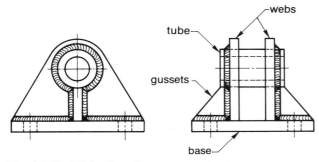

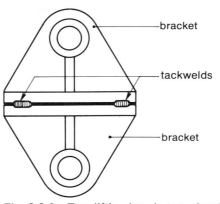

Fig. **2.9.**2   Lifting bracket: two required

Fig. **2.9.**3   Two lifting brackets tackwelded 'back to Back' before final welding

Examples

Fig. **2.9.**2 shows one of a pair of lifting brackets for use with a two-hook chain. The sequence of assembly and welding offers the following options:

Sequence 1
- Set the webs on the base
- Weld the webs to the base
- Fit the tube through the webs and then the gussets in position
- Weld up complete.

This sequence would give the best access for welding the webs to the base, but distortion would leave the webs out of square with the base and cause difficulties in threading the tube through the holes in the lugs.

Sequence 2
- Assemble complete
- Weld up complete.

This sequence ensures that the tube retains the webs at the correct distance apart and the gussets retain the webs at 90° to the base.

Welding would require greater skill and more care. Distortion after welding would cause the corners of the base to curl upwards relative to its centre; some method of restraint must, therefore, be used.

Possible methods of restraint for use in Sequence 2
i   Clamp the base to a heavy plate fixture when welding webs and gussets to the base.
ii With the two bases clamped together at the four corners, proceed with the welding.

iii Tackweld the two assemblies together before welding (Fig. **2.9.**3).

The advantage with method iii is that before the tacks are broken the pair of brackets could be stress relieved by heat treatment, i.e. all locked-up stresses are relieved, giving undistorted fabrication.

The joining of the base plates using bolts is not recommended. The bolts need to be very strong in comparison with the fabrication or difficulty will be met when an attempt is made to unscrew the nuts.

Fig. **2.9.**4a shows the sinkage of the seam in a cylinder as a result of welding. The use of the jacks and supports shown in Fig. **2.9.**4b and c will prevent this.

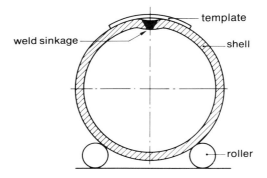

a Illustration of seam sinkage

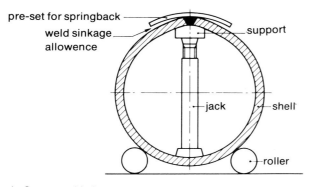

b Support added

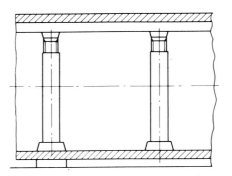

c Seam sinkage prevented by internal restraining (section through b)

Fig. **2.9.**4   Seam sinkage and prevention

Fig. **2.9**.5 shows a welding floor being used for the assembly and finishing welding of large plates. Assembly is carried out on stands to allow access to the underside. Heavy weights assist alignment and also prevent distortion.

2.9.c The applications of pre-setting and restraining

The following situations are likely to be met in most fabrication:
- Components are not flat or straight
- Components are not precisely finished to size or are not completely rolled
- Components are not secure
- Components are prone to move or distort during welding.

2.9.c.i Components not flat or straight

The central web in the saddles shown in Fig. **2.9**.6 forms a tee piece with the baseplate. It is unlikely that these two parts will be flat or straight because of shearing or oxy-gas cutting. The parts must first be

Fig. **2.9**.5   Welding floor

flattened and straightened as far as possible.
A strong, straight 'I section' should be selected with a wider flange than the baseplate. The baseplate should be clamped to the beam flange, using extra clamps to improve the set where it is not level (Fig. **2.9**.7a). The central web should then be tacked in position and reinforced with an angle strut (Fig. **2.9**.7b). Welding can be carried out while these components are still clamped to the 'I section'.

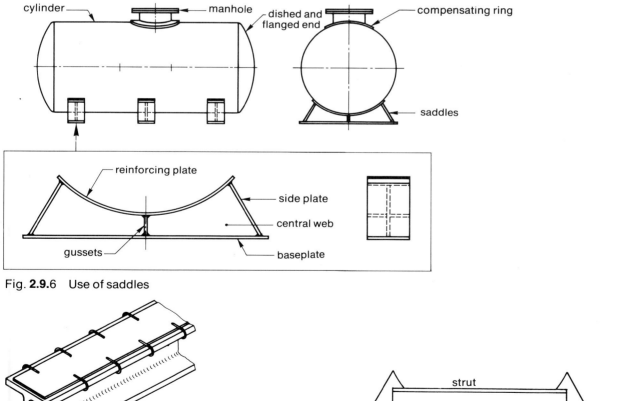

Fig. **2.9**.6   Use of saddles

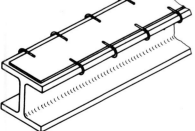

a Baseplate clamped to I section

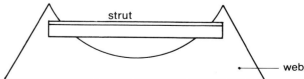

b Preventing movement at the weak part of the web

Fig. **2.9**.7   Restraining

The gussets and side plates should be set on and the welding completed before the strut is removed and the baseplate checked to ensure that it is level. Some distortion will probably take place when the strut is removed. Alternatively, pairs of cradles can be tackwelded 'back to back' for welding.

2.9.c.ii Components partly rolled or imprecisely finished

The reinforcing plates are unlikely to be rolled to the exact form of the cylinder (Fig. **2.9.**8a). It is necessary to set each plate to the profile of the cylinder at the location position. They should be tackwelded in position on the cylinder and each assembly fitted to suit by grinding the web profile before being tackwelded.

Because of distortion when cutting out the manhole, the compensating ring will require setting to the exact cylinder profile. It should be clamped and wedged to form a close fit and tackwelded in position (Fig. **2.9.**8b). Cylinders are rarely truly circular, owing to distortion being introduced when they are lifted from the rolling machine and transported to the assembly area.

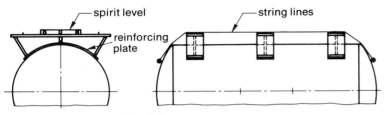

a Reinforcing plate fitting

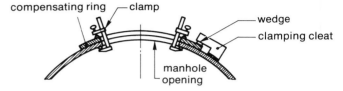

b Setting compensating ring on cylinder

Fig. **2.9.**8   Reinforcing plate and compensating rings

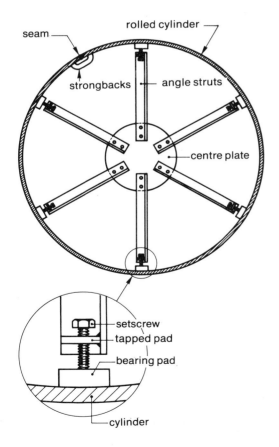

Fig. **2.9.**9   Truing up cylinder with spider attachment

Large thin cylinders can be pre-set, as shown in Fig. **2.9.**9, ready for fitting flanges, dished and flanged ends or for fitting to other lengths of cylinder.

2.9.c.iii Insecure components

Where large openings are cut in rectangular and cylindrical tanks for attachments such as manholes, temporary props should be inserted to prevent movement of the attachment resulting from shrinkage during welding (Fig. **2.9.**10).

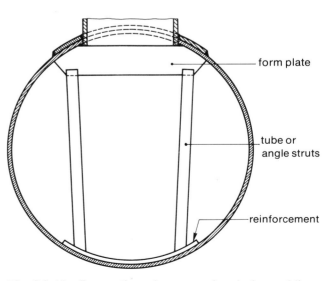

Fig. **2.9.**10   Supporting a large opening during welding

2.9.c.iv Components prone to move or distort in welding

If the prevention of distortion is difficult, methods of pre-setting can be used before assembly. Estimating the amount of distortion allows the parts to be pre-set or pre-formed in such a position that the correct profile and finished size is achieved after welding (Fig. **2.9.**11). Distortion may also be controlled by the assembly and welding sequence.

distortion expected if set up at 90°

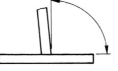
pre-set predicting distortion

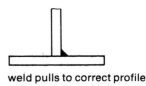
weld pulls to correct profile

a Single welded tee fillet

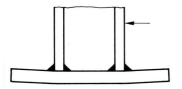
distortion expected if base flat before welding

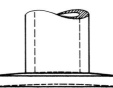
base pre-set by 'dishing' before assembly

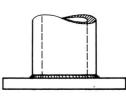
weld pulls base flat

b Circular base welded to tubular support

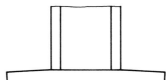
distortion expected if base flat before welding

base pre-set by bending before assembly

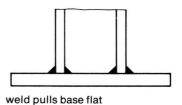
weld pulls base flat

c Rectangular base welded to I section

Fig. **2.9.**11   Distortion anticipated and pre-set to correct

Example

A steel plate 5 mm thick has to be welded to a frame fabricated from the separate pieces shown in Fig. **2.9.**12. Two procedures are possible:

i Assemble and weld the frame only, rectify any distortion, set on the plate and weld.

ii Assemble the separate parts of the frame on to the plate and weld up the complete fabrication.

The method chosen is determined by the amount of welding that needs to be carried out on the frame relative to the plate thickness, the expected distortion and the ease with which it can be controlled. In this case procedure ii would not be carried out, as it is unlikely that the relatively thin plate would restrain the distortion caused by welding the frame and it would be very difficult to straighten the completed fabrication.

Using procedure i the frame could easily be fixed to a solid base and welded. The frame would then provide stiffening for the 5 mm plate and distortion would be limited to the panels between the frame members.

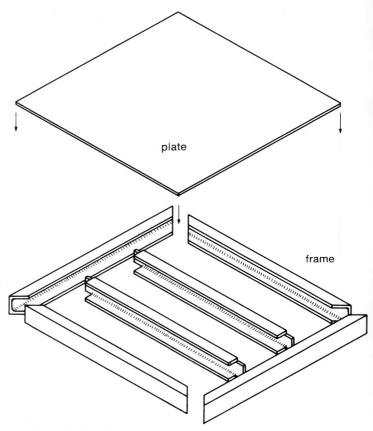

Fig. **2.9.**12   Plate and frame

2.10 Straightening and planishing (flattening)

2.10.a Purpose

The purpose of straightening and planishing (flattening) is to correct unacceptable deviations in straightness or flatness before, during and after assembly. It is applied as a preliminary or finishing operation to salvage components or fabrications that would otherwise be unsuitable for use.

2.10.b Methods of straightening or flattening

These processes can be achieved
- By hand, using suitable hammers or mallets
- Mechanically
  - i   in a set of levelling rolls
  - ii in a section-bending machine
  - iii in a suitable press
- By heating.

Each method will be discussed.

2.10.b.i Straightening and levelling by hand

Some of the tools used are shown in Fig. **2.10.**1. They include:
- ball and cross pein hammers and mallets
- sledge hammers varying in weight from 15 kilograms to 60 kilograms
- flatters to prevent indentation of the component by the hammer
- levelling blocks, thick flat plates or heavy structural sections
- rings or pots.

Before any section or plate is levelled, any twist should be removed. For flat strips and light sections one end is clamped in a vice and the twist removed with the aid of a suitable lever (Fig. **2.10.**2). For heavy sections twist is removed by the application of mechanical force, such as a jack (Fig. **2.10.**3).

2.10.b.i 1 Straightening by hand
Strips, flat bars and some sections can usually be straightened by stretching the concave edge with a series of closely placed hammer blows (Fig. **2.10.**4) whilst the component is held against a solid block.

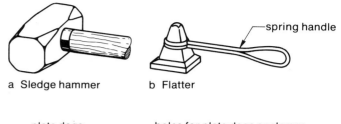

a Sledge hammer   b Flatter

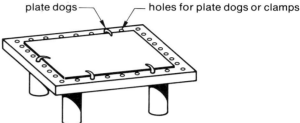

c Plate clamped to levelling block

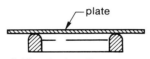

d Ring for levelling component

Fig. **2.10.**1   Tools used for hand straightening and levelling

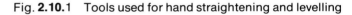

Fig. **2.10.**2   Lever

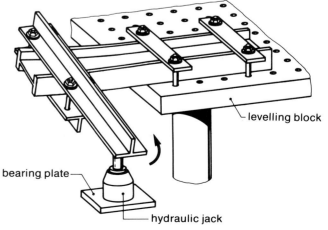

Fig. **2.10.**3   Removing twist with the aid of a jack

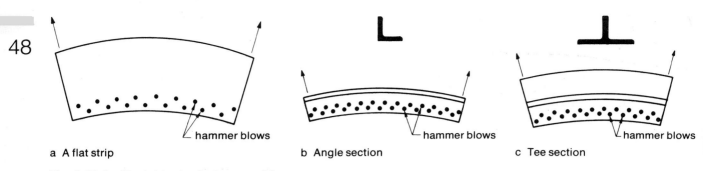

a A flat strip

b Angle section

c Tee section

Fig. **2.10**.4   Straightening by hammer blows

2.10.b.i 2 Levelling by hand

The method will be determined according to which of the following is required.

- *Stretching and upsetting.* The component bears fully on a flat surface (Fig. **2.10.**5). When it is struck by a hammer the material will upset in the direction of the blow, creating forces which cause stretching. The spread of the upsetting force in a cone shape tends to bend the material. The component must be pressed down or clamped during hammering; it must be released and checked at intervals to establish where further hammering is required.

- *Stretching only.* The component bears locally on a support. When it is struck near the centre by a hammer the force exerted between the supports stretches the material over a greater distance, thereby bending the component.

- *Removing local distortion.* In thin plates this can be removed by stretching the area round the buckle (Fig. **2.10.**6). This is done by closely spaced hammer blows working round the buckle in 'rings' and continuing outwards from the distortion, at the same time turning the plate over regularly.

2.10.b.ii Mechanical straightening and levelling

2.10.b.ii 1 In a set of levelling rolls

The roll in Fig. **2.10.**7 incorporates a number of upper and lower rolls. The efficiency of this type of roll is determined by the number of rolls; the more rolls the better the result.

The plate is fed between the upper and lower rolls. The upper rolls are adjustable vertically to bend the plate a number of times over its full width before finally levelling it. The stresses generated are distributed throughout the plate.

2.10.b.ii 2 In a section-bending machine

Straightening of sections and oxy-gas cut strips can be carried out in a section-bending machine (Fig. **2.10.**8).

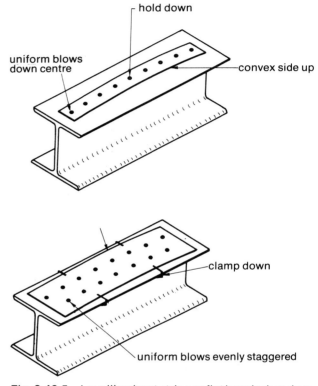

Fig. **2.10.**5   Levelling bent strips or flat bars by hand on a flat support

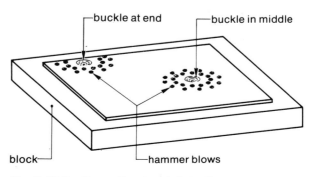

Fig. **2.10.**6   Correcting local distortion

a Industrial levelling roll machine

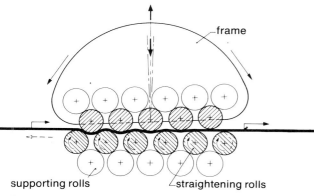

frame

supporting rolls   straightening rolls

b Layout rolls

Fig. **2.10**.7   Levelling rolls

Fig. **2.10**.8   Section-bending machine

49

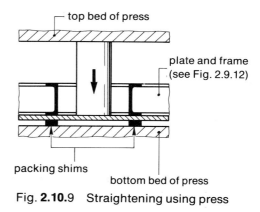

top bed of press

plate and frame
(see Fig. 2.9.12)

packing shims

bottom bed of press

Fig. **2.10**.9   Straightening using press

2.10.b.iii Straightening by heating

This method is usually applied when cold methods fail or on heavy fabrications too thick for hammering or too large for pressing.

Heating can be used to straighten long or short lengths of structural sections when bending machines and presses are not available.

Correction by heating is a lengthy job, requiring patience and practice. Material type, thickness and form can require differing areas of material to be heated.

2.10.b.ii 3 In a press

Presses and press brakes can be used for various types of straightening on plates, sections and fabrications. Pressure is usually applied locally with a flat tool and with packing arranged underneath to 'over-bend' the component or fabrication slightly, allowing it to 'spring back' to the correct profile (Fig. **2.10**.9).

2.10.b.iii 1 The following principles apply to the operation

- Heating causes contraction and stresses.
- Small areas should be heated as the first part of the operation.
- The results should be checked when the material has cooled slowly and reached ambient temperature. This may take from one to several hours, depending upon thickness.

- Extension of the areas or further areas can be decided upon, depending upon the results.
- A circular spot or ring causes contraction in all directions (Figs. **2.10.**10 a and b).
- Heating along straight lines causes contraction in one direction (Fig. **2.10.**10c).
- Heating a triangle on the edge causes that edge to contract (Fig. **2.10.**10d).
- Fabrications made from thick and thin sections require the thick sections to be straightened first.

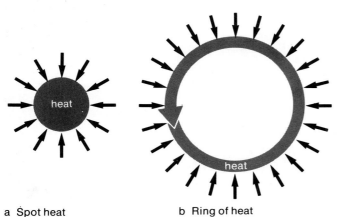

a Spot heat   b Ring of heat   c Straight line of heat   d Heat triangles

Fig. **2.10.**10   Principles of straightening by heating

2.10.b.iii 2 Dealing with contraction and stresses resulting from heating

The procedure is as follows:
- Select the correct heating equipment
  - i   a gas welding blowpipe for thin fabrications
  - ii a blowpipe fitted with a heating nozzle for thick fabrications
- Set the gas pressures as recommended by the equipment suppliers and adjust for a slightly carbonising flame
- Chalk the areas to be heated, heat with the inner cone tip 2 to 4mm from the surface, keeping the flame moving to avoid burning the surface
- Allow to cool naturally; do not quench
- Check the result and decide what further work is needed.

Examples of hot straightening and levelling are shown in Fig. **2.10.**11.

The area to be heated is shaded; if straightening or levelling is not complete, further heat should be applied at point X. The thick arrow indicates the direction of bend.

Safety note. All heating involves hazards. Safety rules must be known and observed.

In particular great care must be taken when using oxy-gas. Safe procedures are discussed in the series book *Fusion Welding*.

To prevent people sustaining accidental burns, the fabrication's heated parts should be marked **HOT** in bold characters.

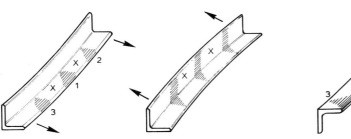
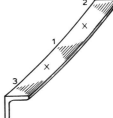

a Angle section

Fig. **2.10.**11   Examples of hot straightening and levelling

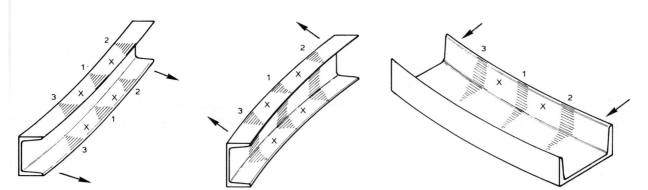

b Channel section

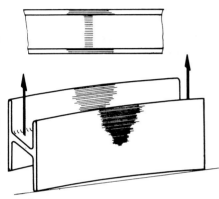
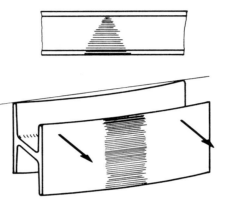

c I Section

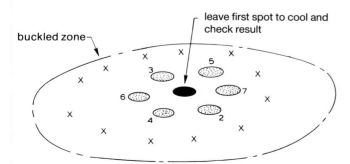

d Levelling a flat bar

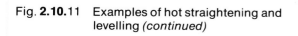

buckled zone

leave first spot to cool and
check result

e Levelling a buckle in a plate

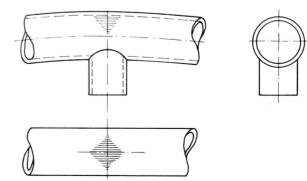

f Straightening a tube distorted by welding a branch pipe

Fig. **2.10.**11   Examples of hot straightening and
levelling *(continued)*

Addendum: Finishing operations and inspection

Finishing operations and inspection

The following observations cover an aspect of fabrication not examined under the City and Guilds of London Institute syllabus, but important in completing fabrication work satisfactorily.

The completed fabrication *must be checked for correct dimensions, form and function in accordance with the working drawing*. It is worth remembering that errors in the assembly are usually easier and cheaper to rectify in the workshop than after final installation at the site.

Technology of Skilled Processes

Basic Engineering
Competences 201

Fabrication

Practice and test questions

Published as a
co-operative venture
between
Stam Press Ltd

and

City and Guilds

Practice and test questions

The questions in this book are intended to help the student achieve and demonstrate a knowledge and understanding of the subject matter covered by this book. Accordingly, the questions follow the original chapter order, under the same headings. Finally there are questions spanning the chapters and approximating to the level of those in the relevant examination of the City and Guilds of London Institute.

FOR THE ATTENTION OF THE TEACHER AND THE STUDENT

The content of this book and the questions for the student have been carefully prepared by a group of special editors in co-operation with the City and Guilds of London Institute. We should like to draw your attention to the copyright clause shown at the beginning of the book, on this page and the following pages:

© STAM PRESS LTD, CHELTENHAM, 1987

First published in Great Britain 1987
as a co-operative venture between Stam Press Ltd
and the City and Guilds of London Institute

Reprinted 1989

© Stam Press Ltd, Cheltenham, 1987

Printed and bound in Great Britain by
Martin's of Berwick

FABRICATION   Name: _____ Class: _____ Number: _____

2.1   The definition and purpose of fabrication

The following questions relate to the above subject, but what is said here about answering them *also* applies to similarly framed questions covering the later subject headings.

Questions like **2.3.**4 require you to choose the correct answer from a number of possible answers. You are required to circle the related letter. Thus if you decide the correct answer is c you show it like this ⓒ.

Example

Crane hooks are manufactured from:

a   mild steel
b   stainless steel
c   cast iron
ⓓ   forged steel

Other questions require short written answers or a sketch.

1   Define fabrication.   _____
                                _____
                                _____
                                _____

2   State TWO requirements relating to safety which must be   _____
    decided before starting work.   _____
                                _____
                                _____

2.2   The stages of fabrication

The question below relates to the above subject. The answer should be given in the form of a list.

1   List the thirteen stages involved in completing a fabrication.

    _____
    _____
    _____
    _____

2.3   Preparation of the working area

The following questions relate to the above subject. Except where otherwise indicated, the correct answers should be given as explained above.

1   State THREE items in addition to the actual fabrication   _____
    which require floor area for assembly.   _____
                                _____
                                _____

2   State THREE services that may be required for   _____
    fabrication.   _____
                                _____
                                _____

3 A single-phase electrical supply is required for:
   a   power for large machines
   b   site heating
   c   welding
   d   power for small power tools

4 A three-phase electrical supply is required for:
   a   power for large machines
   b   hand lamps
   c   diesel engine ignition systems
   d   reducing the danger of electric shock

5 State the TWO essential factors to be considered before using lifting equipment.

   _____

   _____

2.4 Transport of component parts of the fabrication

The following questions relate to the above subject. Except where otherwise indicated, the correct answers should be given as explained on page 55.

1 State FIVE factors which must be considered when selecting the mode of transport for moving a load.

   _____

   _____

   _____

   _____

   _____

   _____

2 State the security checks to be carried out on a–d before fully raising a load:

   a hooks and clamps _____

   b chains and ropes _____

   c workers in the vicinity _____

   d balance of the load _____

3 A load being moved by a crane is prevented from swinging by:
   a steadying with a pole
   b using a guide rope
   c shortening the sling
   d holding the load by hand

4 State how damage to the fabrication, floor and lifting accessories is prevented when the load is lowered:
   a by using rope slings
   b by using chocks
   c by using jacks
   d by lowering the load slowly on to chocks

5 Items 1, 2 and 3 are available for lifting loads a–d. Select the correct one for each and indicate your choice alongside.

   a a 2 m length of rolled steel channel _____   1 two-hook chains _____

   b a circular plate 2 m diameter _____   2 three-hook chains _____

   c an easily balanced load _____   2 chain with two lifting eyes _____

   d an unbalanced load _____

FABRICATION

6 Items 1, 2 and 3 are available for use in situations a–g. Select the most suitable one for each and indicate your choice alongside.

a suspending pulley blocks _____

b lifting a red-hot bar for forging _____

c lifting a copper cylinder _____

d lifting a bundle of steel tubes _____

e lifting a large I beam _____

f lifting a polished stainless steel tank _____

g lifting a load with sharp corners _____

1 fibre rope slings _____

2 wire core slings _____

3 chain slings _____

7 Items 1–6 are available for use in situations a–f. Select the most suitable one for each and indicate your choice alongside.

a turning a plate over _____

b lifting using eyebolts _____

c lifting a plate 2.5 m × 1.5 m × 20 mm thick _____

d attaching to heavy lifting lugs on a fabrication _____

e removing plates from a vertical storage rack _____

f lifting a plate 5 m × 1.5 m × 6 mm thick _____

1 D shackles _____

2 lifting shackles _____

3 vertical lifting clamps _____

4 horizontal plate clamps _____

5 plate lifters _____

6 lifting beams _____

8 From the table of safe working loads shown below select and indicate suitable diameters of slings for lifting:

a 1000 kg using a single fibre rope _____

b 1000 kg using a single wire rope _____

c 1000 kg using a single short link chain _____

d 2000 kg using a pair of short link chains at 90° angle _____

e 2000 kg using a pair of short link chains at 45° angle _____

f 3000 kg using a single short link chain _____

g 3000 kg using a pair of short link chains at 120° angle _____

Table

Maximum load

diameter	steel wire rope	fibre rope	short -link chain	steel wire rope	fibre rope	short -link chain	steel wire rope	fibre rope	short -link chain	steel wire rope	fibre rope	short -link chain	steel wire rope	fibre rope	short -link chain
mm	kN	kN	kN	kN	kN	kN	kN	kN	kN	kN	kN	kN	kN	kN	kN
8	5		6	7·5		9	9·2		11	7		8·5	5		6
10	7·5		9·5	11		14	14		17·5	10		13·5	7·5		9·5
12	10		13·5	15		20	18·5		25	14		19	10		13·5
16	20	2	24	30	3	36	37	3·7	44	28	3	35	20	2	24
20	30	3	38	45	4·5	57	55	5·5	70	42	4	54	30	3	38
24	40	4	54	60	6	81	74	7·5	100	57	6	78	40	4	54
28	60	6	74	90	9	111	109	11	136	85	8·5	105	60	6	74
32	80	8	95	120	12	142·5	147·5	15	175	113	11·5	134	80	8	95
36	100	10	120	150	15	180	184	18·5	220	140	14	170	100	10	120
40	120		150	180		225	220		276	170		210	120		150
44	140		180	210		270	257·5		330	198		260	140		180
48	170		220	255		330	315		410	240		310	170		220

*The figures quoted refer only to steel ropes of the 6 × 24 + 7 construction and of the quoted tensile strength.

9   State where you would find the safe working load exhibited   _____
for a lifting accessory.   _____

_____

10   Give ONE reason for using each of the following:

a   a crowbar   _____

b   screwjacks   _____

c   a hydraulic jack   _____

11   Describe the essential precaution to be taken before working   _____
under a load raised by a jack.   _____

_____

12   Items 1–8 might be used in the situations a–h. Select those most suitable for each and indicate your choice alongside.

a   high lifts on restricted sites _____   1 forklift truck _____

b   moving a fabrication on skates or rollers _____   2 hauling block _____

c   lifting within the full area of a workshop _____   3 pulley block _____

d   lifting light parts of roof frames on site _____   4 chain block _____

e   lifting on a jib arm fitted to a building stanchion _____   5 overhead cranes on gantries _____

f   lifting at different locations on a site _____   6 tower cranes _____

g   lifting during repairs to a ship's superstructure _____   7 mobile cranes _____

h   moving small heavy loads from workshop to workshop ____   8 floating cranes _____

13   State what must be marked on any lifting   _____
equipment to conform with the Factories Act.   _____

_____

_____

14   Label the standard crane signals shown below to indicate instructions being given to the driver.

58

FABRICATION

Name: _____ Class: _____ Number: _____

2.5 Determining the work sequence

The following questions relate to the above subject. Except where otherwise indicated, the correct answers should be given as explained on page 55.

1 Describe how marking out or cutting materials assists the fabricator.

_____

_____

_____

Questions 2, 3 and 4 relate to the figure showing the cover for a small vessel.

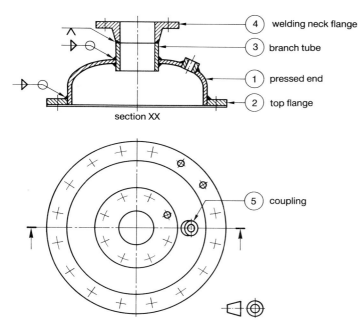

section XX

(4) welding neck flange

(3) branch tube

(1) pressed end

(2) top flange

(5) coupling

2 State why the hot pressed end 1 must be manufactured before rolling the top flange 2.

_____

_____

_____

3 Describe what must be marked out on the welding neck flange, the pressed end and the flange ring to assist the fabricator.

_____

_____

_____

4 State why the branch tube and welding neck flange would be made up as a sub-assembly.

_____

_____

_____

_____

_____

Questions 5, 6 and 7 relate to the figure which shows a switch pocket welded to the side of a transformer tank. The inside size is 300 mm × 100 mm × 80 mm deep.

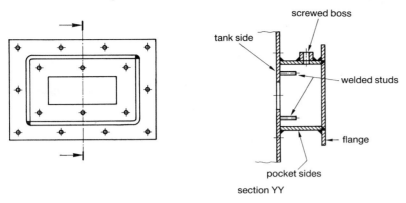

section YY

5   State why the screwed boss would be welded to the pocket
    sides before fitting the flange.

    _____

    _____

    _____

6   State why the flange would be welded to the pocket sides
    before the pocket is welded to the tank side.

    _____

    _____

    _____

7   The other three operations are: welding the pocket to the tank; cutting the opening; welding the studs.
    Put these three operations in the correct sequence and give reasons for your selection.

    i   _____

    ii _____

    iii _____

    _____

FABRICATION

Name: _____ Class: _____ Number: _____

Questions 8–13 relate to the figure which shows the supporting structure for a rectangular grain silo. The structure is to be of all welded construction.

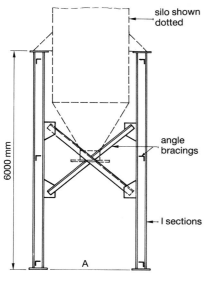

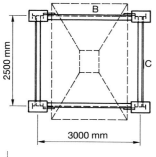

8 State the TWO advantages to be gained by fabricating with side A at the bottom.

   i _____

   ii _____

_____

9 State the possible disadvantage of fabricating in this position.   _____

_____

10 State the advantage of fabricating with side B at the bottom.   _____

_____

11 State the disadvantage of fabricating with side B at the bottom.   _____

_____

12 List the difficulties which could be encountered in transporting this fabrication to the site.   _____

_____

_____

13 List the advantages which would be gained by fabricating this structure as a bolted construction and building it up on site.   _____

_____

_____

2.6 Locating parts to be joined

The following questions relate to the above subject. Except where otherwise indicated, the correct answers should be given as explained on page 55.

Questions 1–7 relate to the figure showing a motor support.

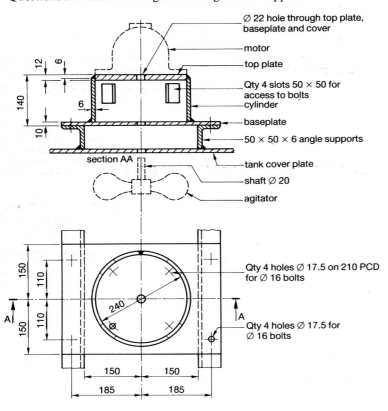

- Ø 22 hole through top plate, baseplate and cover
- motor
- top plate
- Qty 4 slots 50 × 50 for access to bolts
- cylinder
- baseplate
- 50 × 50 × 6 angle supports
- tank cover plate
- shaft Ø 20
- agitator

section AA

Qty 4 holes Ø 17.5 on 210 PCD for Ø 16 bolts

Qty 4 holes Ø 17.5 for Ø 16 bolts

---

1 On the sketches below, mark the datum lines required on each part for accurate assembly.

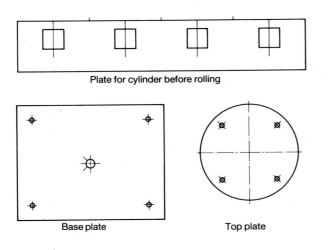

Plate for cylinder before rolling

Base plate   Top plate

---

2 Explain how the setback for the fillet welding of the top plate   _____
to the cylinder can be set up if the top plate is a loose fit.   _____
                                                                       _____

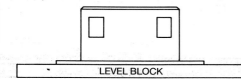

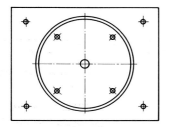

3   Add to the sketch details of the tools to be used when
    carrying out operations a–c.
    a   to check the height of the fabrication before welding
    b   to check that the top and bottom faces are level
    c   to check alignment using the datum lines marked when
        answering question 2.6.1.

4   State how the holes in the top plate and baseplate
    would be set aligned.

5   State the other essential points which should be checked
    before welding.

6   Name TWO tools which can be used to align the holes in the
    baseplate and the angle supports on the tank cover plate.

7   State what should be checked before tightening the bolts
    securing the baseplate to the angle supports.

2.7 Setting up parts to be joined

The following questions relate to the above subject. Except where otherwise indicated, the correct answer should be given as explained on page 55.

Questions 1 and 2 relate to the figure which shows a sub-assembly for a baseplate.

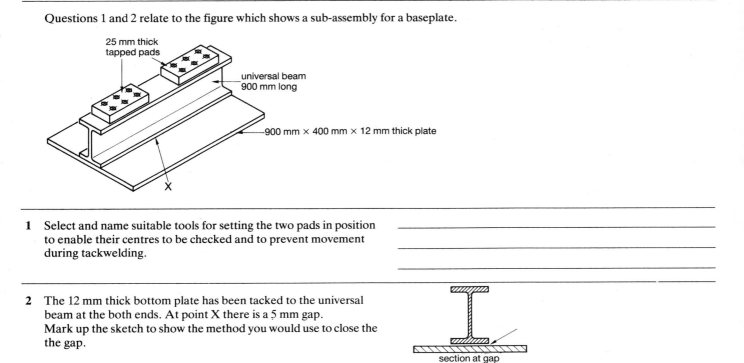

1 Select and name suitable tools for setting the two pads in position to enable their centres to be checked and to prevent movement during tackwelding.

_____

_____

_____

2 The 12 mm thick bottom plate has been tacked to the universal beam at the both ends. At point X there is a 5 mm gap. Mark up the sketch to show the method you would use to close the the gap.

section at gap

Questions 3–7 relate to the figure which shows a compartment mixing and storage tank made from 6 mm thick plate.

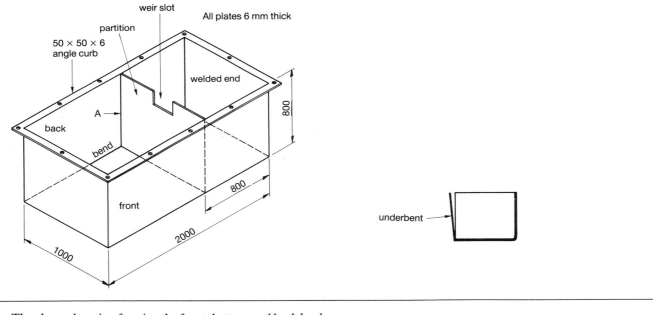

3 The channel section forming the front, bottom and back has been slightly underbent.
Explain briefly how you would close the gap when fitting the end plates.

_____

_____

_____

64

4 The angle curb is a sub-assembly and is a tight fit.
   On the section, sketch suitable equipment to pull it into position
   and ensure that the 8 mm setback for welding is correct.

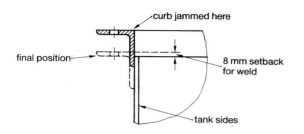

final position—

curb jammed here

8 mm setback
for weld

tank sides

5 The tank is slightly out of square when the angle curb is welded.
   List the equipment you would use to correct this.

_____

_____

_____

6 State the aids that should be used to slide the partition plate
   into the correct position.

_____

_____

7 Make up the sketch to show the equipment required to correct a
   gap at A between the partition plate and the back of the tank to
   enable a fillet weld to be carried out.

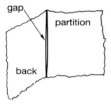

gap

partition

back

Questions 8–14 relate to the figure which shows the cover for the tank considered in Questions 3–6.

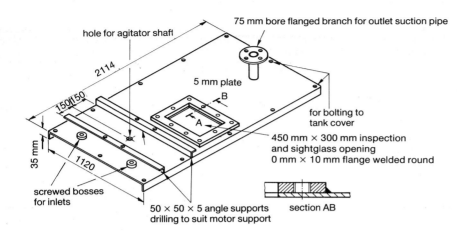

hole for agitator shaft

75 mm bore flanged branch for outlet suction pipe

2114

150 150

5 mm plate

B

35 mm

1120

A

for bolting to
tank cover

450 mm × 300 mm inspection
and sightglass opening
0 mm × 10 mm flange welded round

screwed bosses
for inlets

50 × 50 × 5 angle supports
drilling to suit motor support

section AB

---

8 Name the equipment you would use to clamp the studded pad in position for tackwelding.

At A _____

At B _____

---

9 State how you would hold the 75 mm bore flanged branch at
90° to the cover for tackwelding.

_____

_____

---

10 One angle requires setting vertically to correct a gap at **Y**.
Make up the sketch to show details of the equipment you
would use to achieve this.

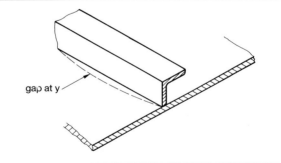

gap at y

---

11 The other angle is bent and requires setting both horizontally and
vertically.
Make up the sketch to show details of the equipment you
would use to do this.

bend in angle

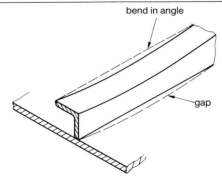

gap

---

12 The motor support referred to in questions 2.6 1–7 is to be
fitted to the two angles. Trial assembly is carried out to check the
hole centres in the angles before welding. State the other point
which should be checked at this stage.

_____

_____

_____

---

13 State how you would maintain the correct centres of the
holes in the angles during welding.

_____

_____

---

14 State TWO types of tool which would be used to line up the   _____
holes in the tank cover with the holes in the tank curb.   _____

Questions 15–19 refer to welded joints with incorrect fit-ups, resulting in faults. Study a–d below, then for each question indicate which fault or faults apply, by writing a, b, c or d in the spaces provided.

a no penetration   c oversize weld
b burn through   d undersize weld

15 Vee-butt weld – excessive gap

i _____   ii _____

16 Tee fillets – gap between plates

i _____   ii _____

17 Open corner weld – gap between plates

i _____   ii _____

18 Vee-butt weld – insufficient gap

i _____   ii _____

19 Open corner weld – plates overlapped

i _____   ii _____

2.8 Fitting

The following questions relate to the above subject. Except where otherwise indicated, the correct answers should be give as explained on page 55.

The figure below shows the assembly and parts of a number of brackets to carry a 6.00 mm diameter pipe along a workshop. To enable assembly of the brackets to be completed, fitting is necessary to correct inaccuracies.

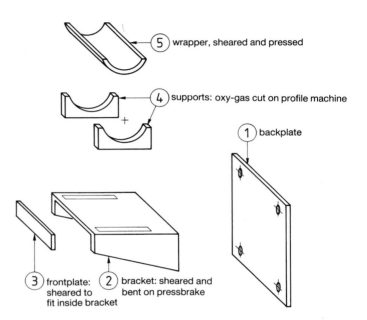

Assembly of support brackets for 600 mm diameter pipe. 6 mm plate

⑤ wrapper, sheared and pressed

④ supports: oxy-gas cut on profile machine

① backplate

③ frontplate: sheared to fit inside bracket   ② bracket: sheared and bent on pressbrake

In Questions 1–5 you are in each one required to describe the checking and fitting operations you would expect to carry out on the parts named.

1 The backplate – this has been sheared and drilled for bolting to the stanchions.   _____

2 The bracket – this has been sheared and bent using a pressbrake and must be set at 90° to the backplate.   _____

3 The frontplate – this has been sheared and is required to fit inside the bracket.   _____

4 The supports – these have been cut out on the oxy-gas profile machine.   _____

5 The wrapper – this has been sheared to size and rolled to shape.   _____

6 Selective assembly could be used in some of the operations referred to in Questions 1–5. State when this would be appropriate.   _____

2.9 Pre-setting and restraining during and after assembly

The following questions relate to the above subject. Except where otherwise indicated, the correct answers should be given as explained on page 55.

1   State the TWO methods of obtaining the correct form of a
    welded fabrication.

2   State the TWO causes of distortion in a welded fabrication.

3   State THREE faults causing excessive distortion.

Questions 4–10 all relate to the figure below, which shows one of a set of four supporting stools 450 mm high. During the fabrication distortion due to welding must be considered.

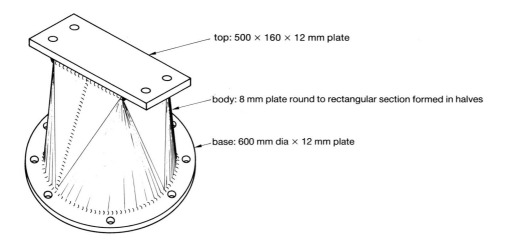

top: 500 × 160 × 12 mm plate

body: 8 mm plate round to rectangular section formed in halves

base: 600 mm dia × 12 mm plate

---

4 The sketch shows a view of the rectangular end of the body, with the top plate removed.

  a Indicate the weld distortion you would expect, using dotted lines.

  b Mark up the sketch to show how pre-setting could be achieved.

  c Describe or sketch how restraint could be carried out.

_____

_____

_____

_____

_____

_____

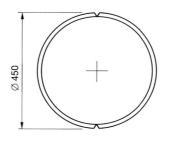

300

150

---

5 The figure shows a view on the bottom of the round end of the body.

  a Using dotted lines indicate the weld distortion you would expect.

  b Mark up the sketch to show the pre-set shape required.

  c Describe or show by marking up the sketch how restraint could be carried out.

_____

_____

_____

_____

_____

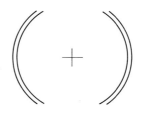

Ø 450

---

6 The sketch shows a section through the fabrication.

 a Using dotted lines indicate the weld distortion you would expect, bearing in mind that the 5 mm fillet welds on the long side of the top should be carried out before the ends are ‑welded.

 b Assume a heavy press was available and complete the sketches to show pre-setting of the top and bottom.

7 If the parts referred to in Question 6 could not be pre-set, describe or sketch how you would prevent distortion.

_____

_____

_____

8 The figure shows an impeller made from 5 mm thick plate. Describe how you would restrain the fabrication to prevent distortion during welding; add the necessary details to the drawing.

_____

_____

_____

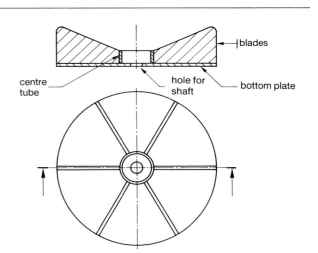

9 Describe the operation which must be carried out on curved or formed plates before tacking to cylinders or domes.

_____
_____

10 Explain why a 'spider' is used when assembling parts to thin cylinders.

_____
_____

11 List the precautions to be taken before cutting large openings and fitting connections to cylinders or ducting.

_____
_____
_____

71

FABRICATION Name: ______ Class: ______ Number: ______

2.10 Straightening and planishing (flattening)

The following questions relate to the above subject. Except where otherwise indicated, the correct answers should be given as explained on page 55.

1 Explain why a flatter is used with a hammer.

2 Mark up the sketch to show TWO methods of clamping a thick plate to a levelling block.

plate
block

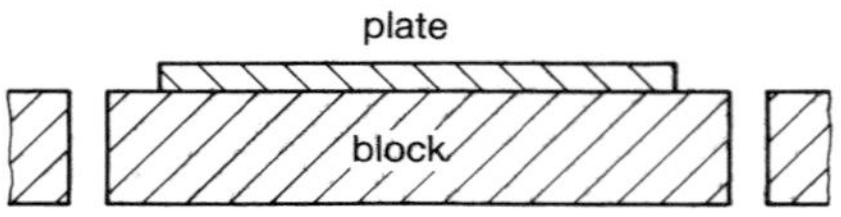

3 Describe the operation to be carried out before levelling a plate or section.

4 In the figure mark with a series of crosses the position of hand hammer blows to straighten or level the parts.

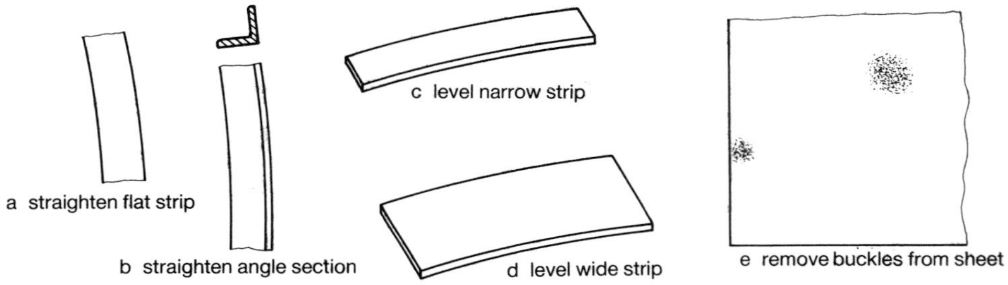

a straighten flat strip
b straighten angle section
c level narrow strip
d level wide strip
e remove buckles from sheet

5 State the appropriate machine required in a, b and c below.

a to level large plates ______

b to straighten sections ______

c to straighten fabrications ______

6 On the examples given in the figure, number the sequence of heating the shaded areas to carry out straightening.

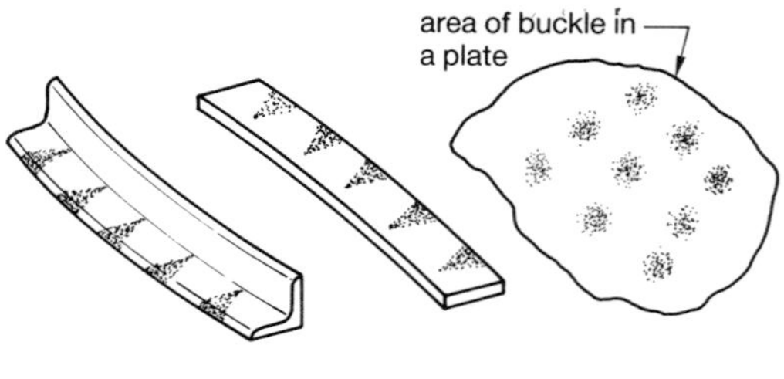

area of buckle in a plate

7 State the essential safety precaution to be taken after heat has been applied for straightening.

FABRICATION

Name: _____ Class: _____ Number: _____

The following questions span the syllabus subject matter and approximate to the level of those in the relevant examination paper of the City and Guilds of London Institute. Answers should be short and clear.

1 State what you understand is meant by a fabrication. _____
_____
_____

2 One of the stages of any fabrication work is 'preparation of the working area'. What do you understand this to mean?
_____
_____
_____
_____

3 Indicate, by circling a, b, c or d, the safe lift that an adult man may handle without recourse to mechanical aids.
   a 80 kg
   b 50 kg
   c 20 kg
   d 30 kg

4 An item of equipment is too heavy to be moved manually. You have the choice of a forklift, mobile crane (motorised on a vehicle chassis) and a gantry.
List the factors you would consider before deciding on a method.

_____
_____
_____
_____
_____

5 In what circumstances would an auxiliary hook be used in conjunction with a main chain hook?
_____
_____
_____

6 If a chain is trapped beneath a load when it is lowered damage may occur. What precautions can be taken to guard against this contingency? Draw a sketch to illustrate your answer.

_____
_____
_____
_____

7 Indicate the correct answer by circling a, b, c or d.
   A wire rope is lubricated:
   a with an oil can
   b by the application of special resin
   c during manufacture
   d before each lift

8 With the aid of a sketch, explain in what circumstances a lifting beam is used.

_____
_____
_____

9 There is a relationship between the safe working load and the jib of a tower crane and that of a derrick. Explain this relationship with the aid of sketches.

_____

_____

_____

_____

_____

_____

10 List FOUR types of accessory used in chocking.

_____

_____

_____

_____

_____

11 List SIX important factors that determine the sequence of fabrication work.

i _____

ii _____

iii _____

iv _____

v _____

vi _____

12 A shaft has to be supported by two bearing blocks, each mounted on a separate metal girder that spans a work area. With the aid of a sketch and a flow diagram explain the sequence of operations necessary to position the shaft so as to ensure free rotation within the bearing blocks.

_____

_____

_____

_____

_____

_____

_____

_____

13 During fabrication a number of identical pieces are to be manufactured. Describe why in appropriate circumstances only the first piece needs to be marked out using measuring devices.

_____

_____

_____

_____

14 Explain the use of tackwelding and the provision that must be made for positioning the tackweld.

_____

_____

_____

_____

15 Define the term 'correct setting up' of welded joints.

_____

_____

_____

16 List SIX methods of fitting to size during fabrication.

i _____   iv _____

ii _____   v _____

iii _____   vi _____

17 State the purpose of:

i Restraining _____

_____

ii Pre-setting _____

_____

18 List THREE methods of mechanically straightening or flattening.

_____

_____

_____

19 Explain the terms 'stretching' and 'upsetting'.

_____

_____

_____

_____

_____

_____

20 List SIX principles of straightening by heating. Illustrate your answer with sketches.

_____

_____

_____

_____

_____

_____